The Education Center, Inc.'s

Forms For All Reasons

Grades K–6

Written by:
Cindy Newell

Edited by:
Jennifer Overend

Copyedited by:
Debbie Blaylock
Lynn B. Coble

Illustrated by:
Teresa Davidson

Typography by:
Lynette Maxwell

About This Book

Forms For All Reasons is your key to classroom organization. This book offers more than 150 helpful forms including charts, posters, planning sheets, parent letters, awards, and much more to assist you throughout the school year. This is a book you don't want to be without!

www.themailbox.com

Manufactured in the United States
10 9

Table Of Contents

Management

Calendars 4–15
First-day checklist 16
First-week checklist 17
Traditional seating chart 18
Cooperative-group seating chart 19
Class information chart 20
Transportation list 21
Bus safety rules 22
Classroom rules 23
Cafeteria rules 24
Behavior policy poster 25
Discipline policy poster 26
Homework policy poster 27
Behavior and discipline policies 28
Homework policy 29
Activity schedule 30
Special class schedule 31
Student information cards 32
Nametags 33
Class jobs 34–35
Job checklists and open job cards 36–37
Book checkout forms 38
Book nameplates 39
Passes 40
Coupons and tokens 41
Attendance report 42
Behavior documentation 43
Room inventory 44

Instruction

Lesson plan sheet part 1 (Pri.) 46
Lesson plan sheet part 2 (Pri.) 47
Lesson plan sheet part 1 (Int.) 48
Lesson plan sheet part 2 (Int.) 49
Subject lesson plan sheet 50
Thematic unit planning sheet 51
Daily planning sheets 52
Grade book sheet 53
Open chart 54
Test sheets 55
Timed evaluation sheet 56
Substitute folder: Cover and checklist 57
Substitute folder: Class information 58
Substitute folder: Procedures 59
Substitute folder: Lesson plans 60
Substitute folder: School map 61
Substitute folder: Staff list 62
Substitute folder: Notepaper 63
Homework kits 64–65
Homework kits letters 66–67
Homework plans 68–69
Cooperative-learning job cards 70–71
Cooperative-group planning sheets 72–73
Cooperative-learning progress chart 74
Punch-out cards 75
Special needs chart 76
Self-evaluation sheets 77–78
Portfolio cover 79
Portfolio assessment record 80
Portfolio conference reports 81–82

All about me (Pri.) 83
Introducing (Int.) 84
Journal pages 85–86
Reading contracts 87–88
Reading group charts 89
Reading take-home slips 90–91
Home reading records 92–93
Book report forms 94–95
Research contracts 96–97
Research planners 98–99
Science lab guide (Pri.) 100
Science lab report (Int.) 101
Student lab chart 102
Science fair entry forms 103
Science project planner 104
Science fair student evaluation 105
Science fair student evaluations 106

Communications

Welcome letters 108–109
Teacher messages from the office 110
Student messages from the office 111
Teacher assistant requests 112
Midterm progress report 113
Weekly progress reports 114–115
Grade reports 116–117
Absence and tardy reports 118
Conference notices 119
Preconference questionnaire 120
Conference schedule 121
Parent/teacher conference report 122
Student/parent conference reports 123–124
Missed assignments 125
Incomplete work 126
Overdue assignments 127
Extra help needed 128
Notes of concern 129
Field trip forms 130–131
Permission to stay after school 132
Money due forms 133
Special program 134
Special TV program 135
Injury reports 136
Broken rule notices 137
No school notices 138
Requests for school supplies 139–140
Art materials requests 141
Special project supplies 142
Reminder notices 143
Class newsletter 144
Parent volunteer information 145
Invitations 146
Halloween party 147
Christmas party 148
Valentine party 149
Celebration 150
Get-well coloring page 151
Thank-you certificates 152
Awards 153–158
Certificates of promotion 159–160

Management

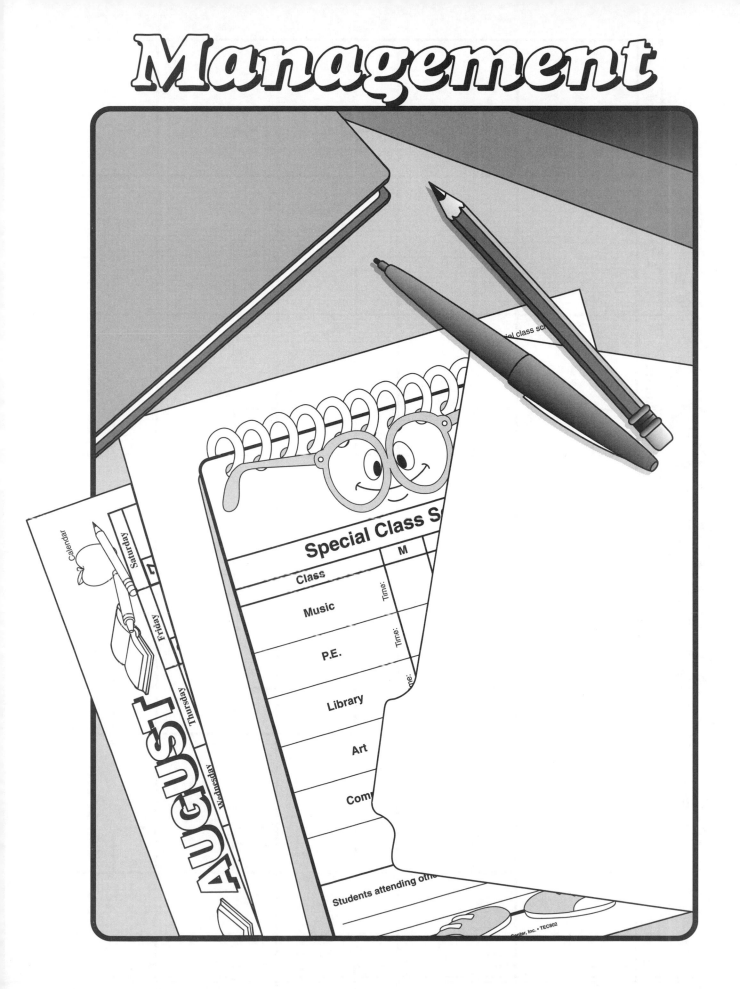

AUGUST

Sunday	Monday	Tuesday	Wednesday	Thursday	Friday	Saturday

SEPTEMBER

Sunday	Monday	Tuesday	Wednesday	Thursday	Friday	Saturday

OCTOBER

Sunday	Monday	Tuesday	Wednesday	Thursday	Friday	Saturday

NOVEMBER

Sunday	Monday	Tuesday	Wednesday	Thursday	Friday	Saturday

DECEMBER

Sunday	Monday	Tuesday	Wednesday	Thursday	Friday	Saturday

JANUARY

Sunday	Monday	Tuesday	Wednesday	Thursday	Friday	Saturday

FEBRUARY

Sunday	Monday	Tuesday	Wednesday	Thursday	Friday	Saturday

APRIL

Sunday	Monday	Tuesday	Wednesday	Thursday	Friday	Saturday

MAY

Sunday	Monday	Tuesday	Wednesday	Thursday	Friday	Saturday

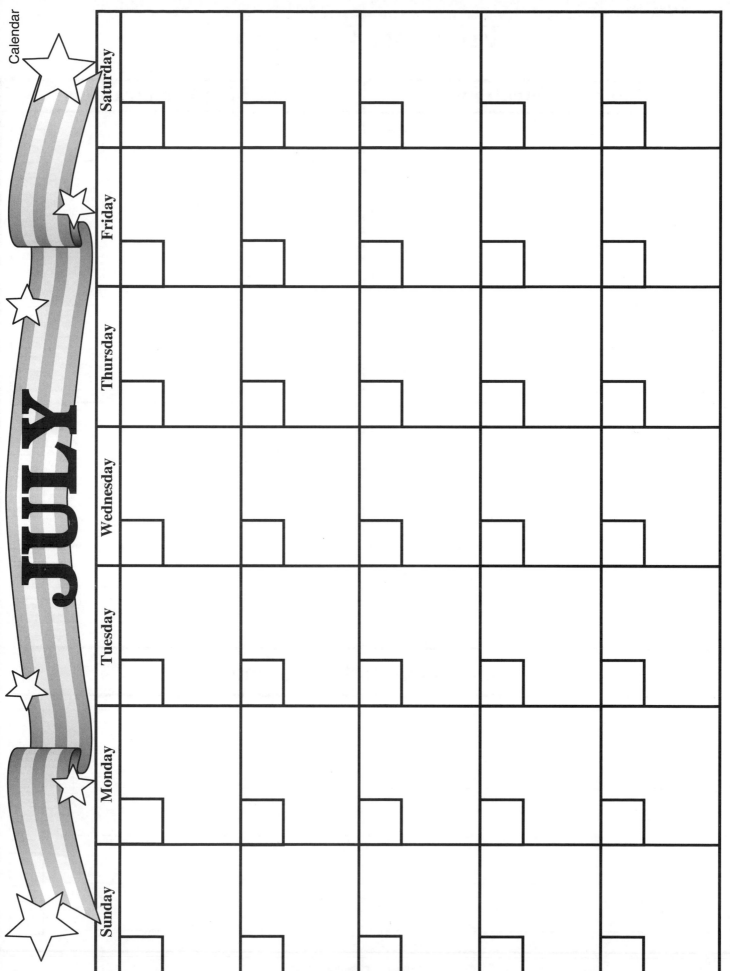

Calendar

JULY

Sunday	Monday	Tuesday	Wednesday	Thursday	Friday	Saturday

First-Day Checklist

Room Preparations		Teaching Preparations	
_____	☐	_____	☐
_____	☐	_____	☐
_____	☐	_____	☐
_____	☐	_____	☐
_____	☐	_____	☐
_____	☐	_____	☐
_____	☐	_____	☐
_____	☐	_____	☐
_____	☐	_____	☐
_____	☐	_____	☐

Communications (office, parents, etc.)

_____	☐
_____	☐
_____	☐
_____	☐
_____	☐

First-Week Checklist

M _____ ☐ ☐ ☐ ☐

T _____ ☐ ☐ ☐ ☐

W _____ ☐ ☐ ☐ ☐

T _____ ☐ ☐ ☐ ☐

F _____ ☐ ☐ ☐ ☐

Comments

_____
_____
_____
_____
_____
_____

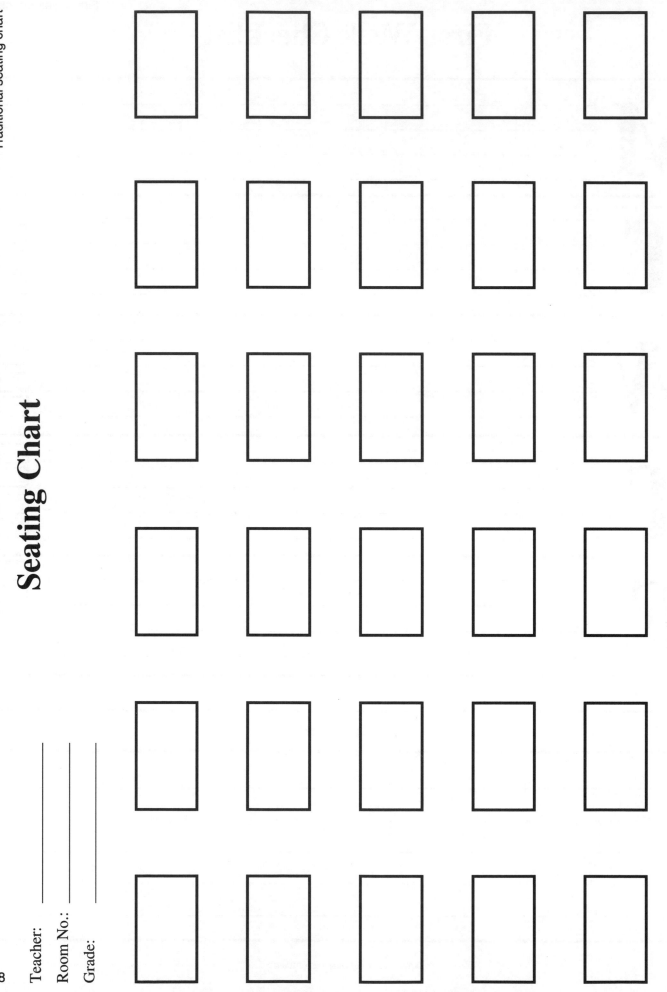

Seating Chart

Teacher: _____

Room No.: _____

Grade: _____

18

Seating Chart

Teacher: _____

Room No.: _____

Grade: _____

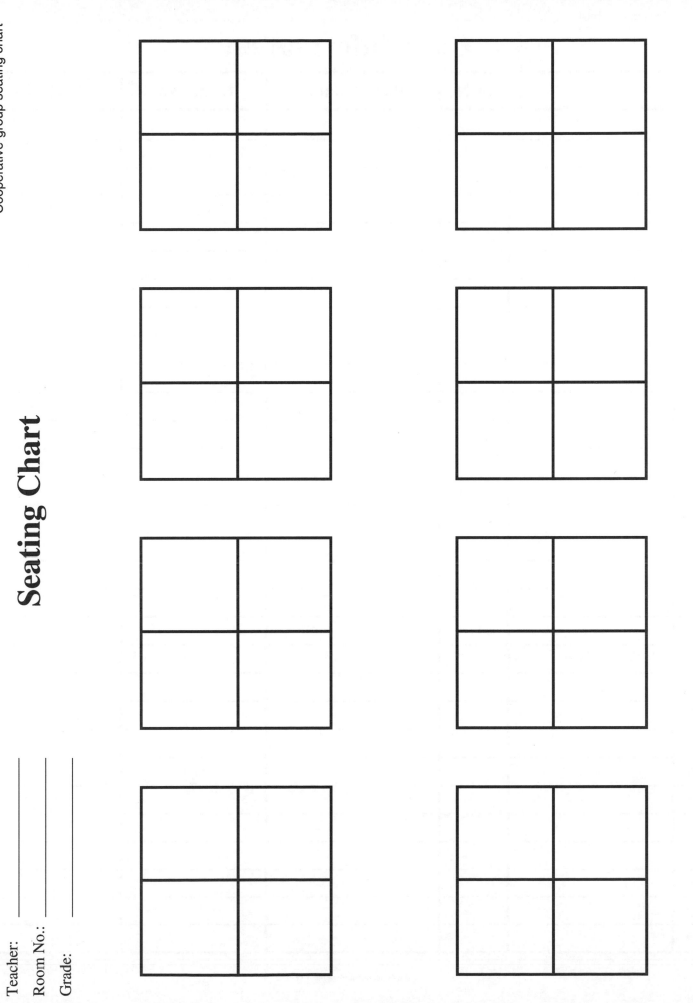

Class Information

	Name	Bus No.	Parent Name	Home No.	Work No.
1.					
2.					
3.					
4.					
5.					
6.					
7.					
8.					
9.					
10.					
11.					
12.					
13.					
14.					
15.					
16.					
17.					
18.					
19.					
20.					
21.					
22.					
23.					
24.					
25.					
26.					
27.					
28.					
29.					
30.					

Transportation List

Teacher: _____

Room No.: _____

Grade: _____

Bus Riders　　　　　　　　　　　　**Bus #**

Walkers

Car Riders

21

BUS SAFETY RULES

Riding the bus is a privilege. Our goal is to safely transport students. To help us achieve this goal, students will:

ABC-123

Our Classroom Rules

We have discussed the rules we need in order to have a positive learning environment.
We agree to:

_____

_____

_____

_____

_____

OUR CAFETERIA RULES

We want our cafeteria to be a pleasant
place to eat. To keep the cafeteria clean
and orderly, we agree to:

_____

_____

_____

_____

_____

Rewards

Behavior Policy

Note To Teacher: Duplicate this page; then use it to display your behavior policy. If desired, enlarge and color this page before displaying it.

Discipline Policy

Severe situations will be handled by:

©The Education Center, Inc. • TEC802

Note To Teacher: Duplicate this page; then use it to display your discipline policy. If desired, enlarge and color this page before displaying it.

Homework Policy

_____

_____

_____

_____

_____

_____

_____

_____

_____

Rewards:

_____

_____

_____

_____

Note To Teacher: Duplicate this page; then use it to display your homework policy. If desired, enlarge and color this page before displaying it.

27

Behavior And Discipline Policies

Dear Parent,

Your child's success is very important. To create and maintain a positive learning environment for all students, I will follow the behavior and discipline policies below. Please read them and discuss them with your child. **Then sign the lower portion of this form and return it to school with your child.** Be sure to keep this portion of the form for future reference.

Behavior Policy

_____
_____
_____
_____

Rewards for good behavior: _____
_____

Discipline Policy

_____
_____
_____
_____
_____
_____

Sincerely,

_____
teacher signature

_____
date

- -

I have read and understood the behavior and discipline policies. I have also discussed these policies with my child.

_____   _____   _____
parent signature   date   student name

- -

Note To Teacher: Duplicate a copy of this page and program the necessary information. Then duplicate copies for your students' parents.

Homework Policy

Dear Parent,

Homework is an important part of your child's school experience. Supporting good work habits requires a joint effort. I will support your child and encourage good work habits at school. Your child will benefit greatly from your support and encouragement at home.

Please read the homework policy below and discuss it with your child. **Then sign the lower portion of this form and return it to school with your child.** Be sure to keep this portion of the form for future reference.

Homework Policy

_____

_____

_____

_____

_____

_____

_____

Rewards: _____

_____

_____

Sincerely,

_____
teacher signature

_____
date

- -

I have read the homework policy. I have also discussed the policy with my child.

_____   _____   _____
parent signature   date   student name

teacher

grade

Activity Schedule

Time	Activity	M	T	W	T	F
–						
–						
–						
–						
–						
–						
–						
–						
–						
–						
–						
–						
–						
–						
–						
–						
–						

teacher

grade

Special Class Schedule

Class		M	T	W	T	F
Music	Time:					
P.E.	Time:					
Library	Time:					
Art	Time:					
Computer	Time:					
	Time:					

Students attending other classes (speech, band, etc.): _____

_____

_____

Student Information Card

Student No.

First name   Last name

Address

City   State   Zip

Mother's name   Father's name   Home phone

Mother's work phone   Father's work phone   Student's birthdate

Comments:

Medical concerns:

In an emergency call:

©The Education Center, Inc. • TEC802

Student Information Card

Student No.

First name   Last name

Address

City   State   Zip

Mother's name   Father's name   Home phone

Mother's work phone   Father's work phone   Student's birthdate

Comments:

Medical concerns:

In an emergency call:

©The Education Center, Inc. • TEC802

©The Education Center, Inc. • TEC802

©The Education Center, Inc. • TEC802

©The Education Center, Inc. • TEC802

©The Education Center, Inc. • TEC802

©The Education Center, Inc. • TEC802

TODAY'S GUEST STAR!

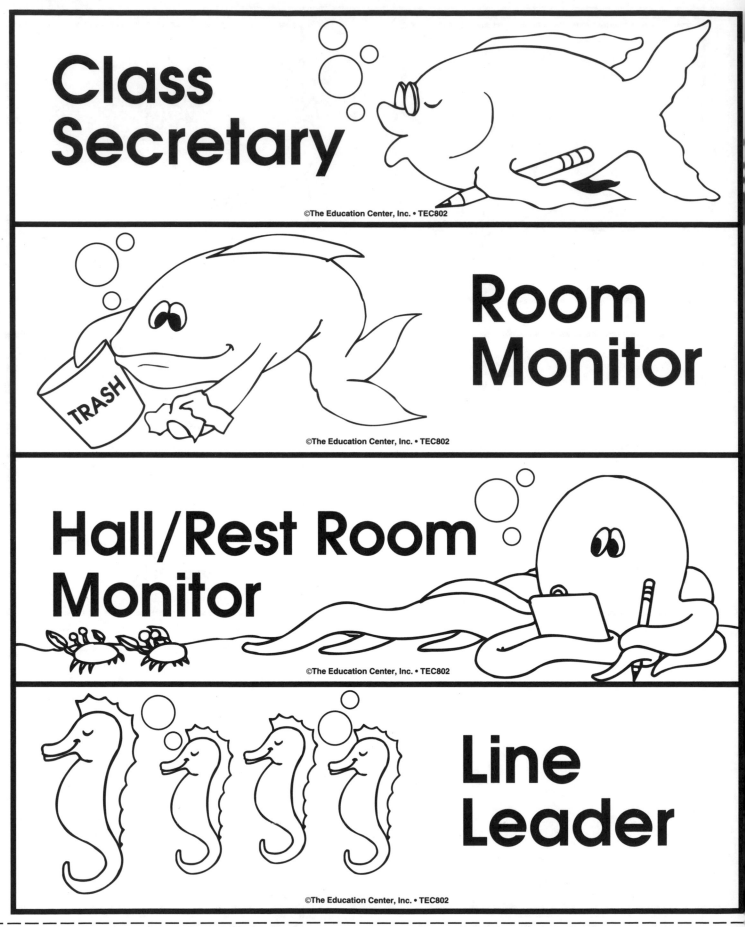

Class Secretary

©The Education Center, Inc. • TEC802

Room Monitor

©The Education Center, Inc. • TEC802

Hall/Rest Room Monitor

©The Education Center, Inc. • TEC802

Line Leader

©The Education Center, Inc. • TEC802

Note To Teacher: Duplicate the job cards on construction paper. Cut the cards apart and glue each one to the front of a legal-size envelope. Display the envelopes on a wall or bulletin board. (See Note To Teacher on page 36 for additional procedures.)

Class Secretary

Runs errands.
Takes notes.
Assists the teacher.

_____

©The Education Center, Inc. • TEC802

Class Clerk

Passes out papers.
Collects papers.
Files papers.

_____

©The Education Center, Inc. • TEC802

Room Monitor

Checks the neatness of the room.
Empties the pencil sharpener.
Cleans the chalkboard and the erasers.

_____

©The Education Center, Inc. • TEC802

Hall Monitor

Observes class behavior in the hallways.
Observes class behavior during breaks.

_____

©The Education Center, Inc. • TEC802

Note To Teacher: Duplicate the job cards on construction paper. Cut the cards apart and glue each one to the front of a legal-size envelope. Display the envelopes on a wall or bulletin board. (See Note To Teacher on page 37 for additional procedures.)

_____
name

Check jobs performed:

_____ Class Secretary

_____ Room Monitor

_____ Hall/Rest Room
        Monitor

_____ Line Leader

_____ _____

_____ _____

_____ _____

©The Education Center, Inc. • TEC802

_____
name

Check jobs performed:

_____ Class Secretary

_____ Room Monitor

_____ Hall/Rest Room
        Monitor

_____ Line Leader

_____ _____

_____ _____

_____ _____

©The Education Center, Inc. • TEC802

_____
name

Check jobs performed:

_____ Class Secretary

_____ Room Monitor

_____ Hall/Rest Room
        Monitor

_____ Line Leader

_____ _____

_____ _____

_____ _____

©The Education Center, Inc. • TEC802

Open job card

©The Education Center, Inc. • TEC802

Open job card

©The Education Center, Inc. • TEC802

Note To Teacher: Duplicate a checklist for each of your students. Cut out the cards and write students' names on them. Each day, place a different student's card in a job envelope (see page 34). Have the student write a √ next to the completed job at the end of the day.

_____
name

Check jobs performed:

_____ Class Secretary

_____ Class Clerk

_____ Room Monitor

_____ Hall Monitor

_____ _____

_____ _____

_____ _____

©The Education Center, Inc. • TEC802

_____
name

Check jobs performed:

_____ Class Secretary

_____ Class Clerk

_____ Room Monitor

_____ Hall Monitor

_____ _____

_____ _____

_____ _____

©The Education Center, Inc. • TEC802

_____
name

Check jobs performed:

_____ Class Secretary

_____ Class Clerk

_____ Room Monitor

_____ Hall Monitor

_____ _____

_____ _____

_____ _____

©The Education Center, Inc. • TEC802

Open job card

©The Education Center, Inc. • TEC802

Open job card

©The Education Center, Inc. • TEC802

Note To Teacher: Duplicate a checklist for each of your students. Cut out the cards and write students' names on them. Each day, place a different student's card in a job envelope (see page 35). Have the student write a √ next to the completed job at the end of the day.

Book checkout cards

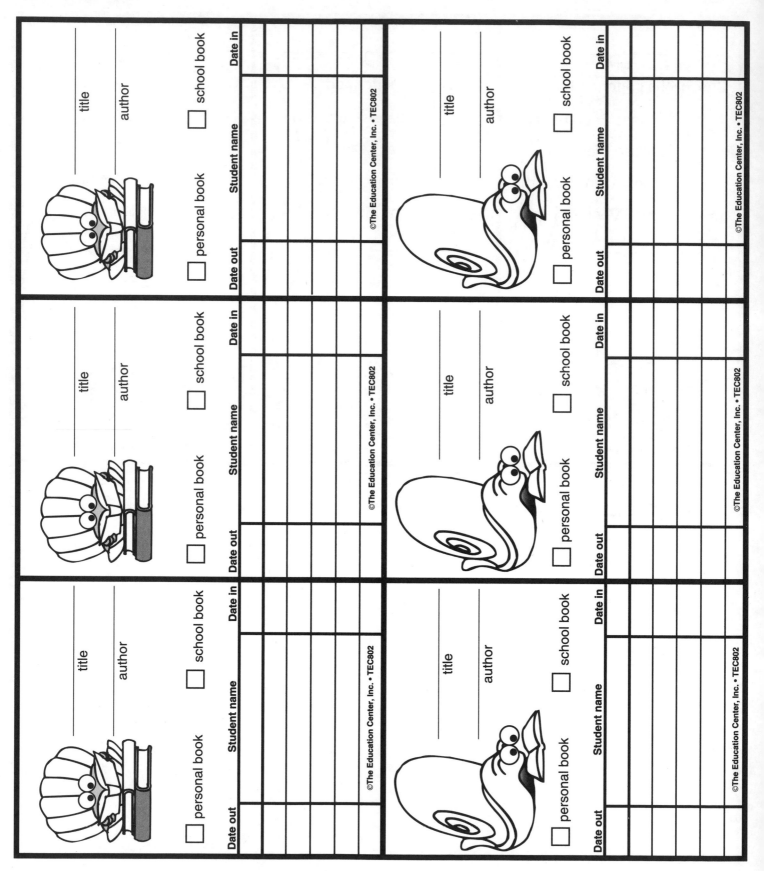

Each checkout card contains:
- title (line)
- author (line)
- ☐ personal book ☐ school book
- Student name | Date out | Date in
- ©The Education Center, Inc. • TEC802

Note To Teacher: Duplicate copies of this page; then cut the cards apart. Attach a library pocket to the inside cover of each of your books. Place a checkout card in each pocket.

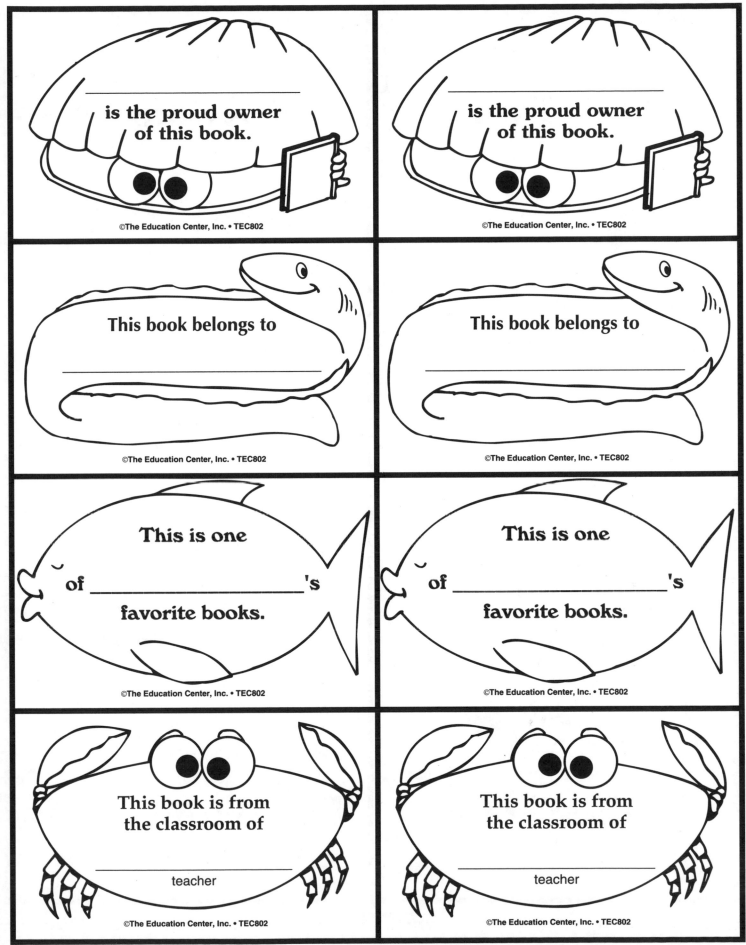

is the proud owner of this book.

©The Education Center, Inc. • TEC802

is the proud owner of this book.

©The Education Center, Inc. • TEC802

This book belongs to

©The Education Center, Inc. • TEC802

This book belongs to

©The Education Center, Inc. • TEC802

This is one of _____'s favorite books.

©The Education Center, Inc. • TEC802

This is one of _____'s favorite books.

©The Education Center, Inc. • TEC802

This book is from the classroom of

teacher

©The Education Center, Inc. • TEC802

This book is from the classroom of

teacher

©The Education Center, Inc. • TEC802

Hall Pass

S.S. HALL

teacher

Rest Room Pass

BUOYS   GULLS

teacher

Office Pass

OFFICE

teacher

Telephone Pass

teacher

Note To Teacher: Duplicate this page. Color the passes as desired. Cut out the cards and then laminate them for durability. Using a hole puncher, punch a hole in the top of each pass. Tie a length of yarn through each hole.

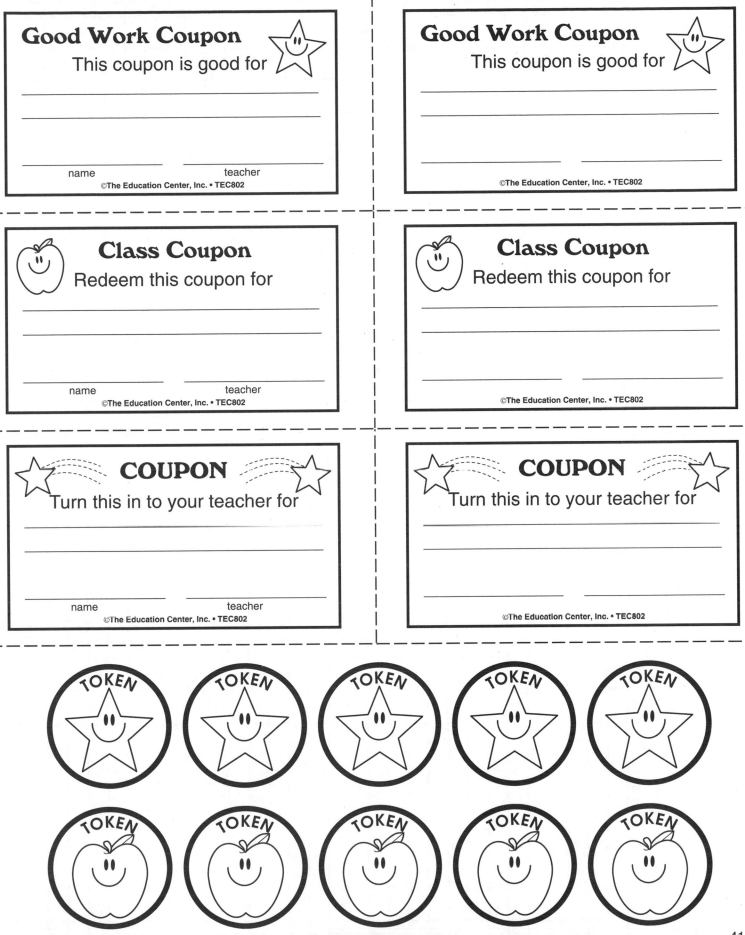

Good Work Coupon

This coupon is good for

_____

_____

_____

name   teacher

©The Education Center, Inc. • TEC802

Good Work Coupon

This coupon is good for

_____

_____

_____

©The Education Center, Inc. • TEC802

Class Coupon

Redeem this coupon for

_____

_____

_____

name   teacher

©The Education Center, Inc. • TEC802

Class Coupon

Redeem this coupon for

_____

_____

_____

©The Education Center, Inc. • TEC802

COUPON

Turn this in to your teacher for

_____

_____

_____

name   teacher

©The Education Center, Inc. • TEC802

COUPON

Turn this in to your teacher for

_____

_____

_____

©The Education Center, Inc. • TEC802

TOKEN   TOKEN   TOKEN   TOKEN   TOKEN

TOKEN   TOKEN   TOKEN   TOKEN   TOKEN

Attendance Report

Period/Subject: _____
Grade: _____ Room No.: _____
Teacher: _____
Date: _____

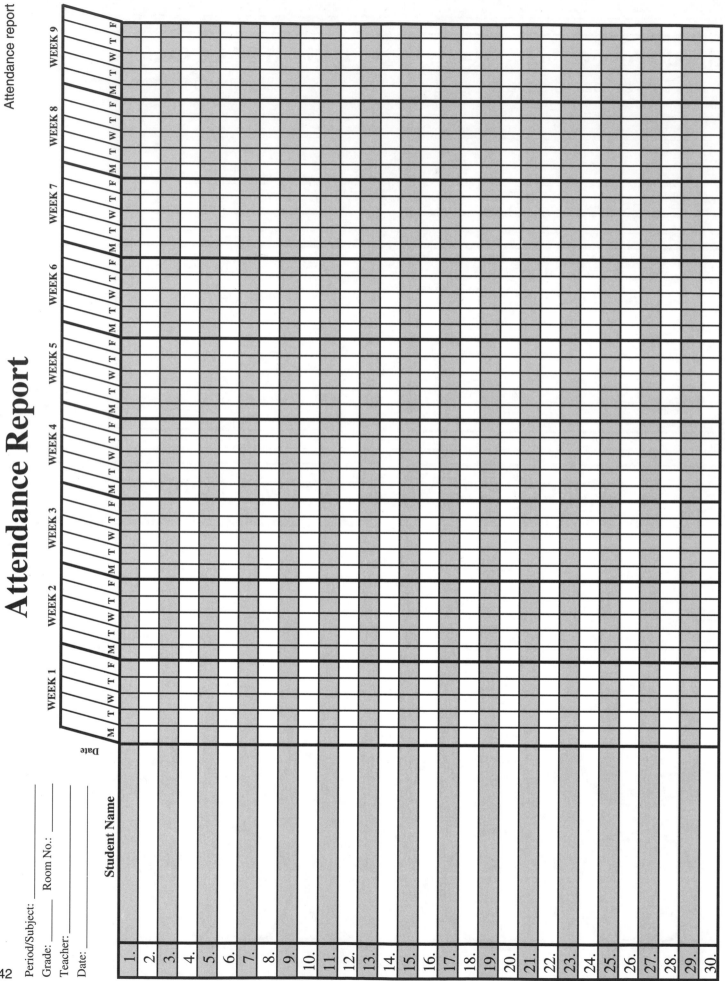

42

Behavior Documentation

Grade: _____ Room No.: _____ Teacher: _____

Period/Subject: _____ Dates: _____

Student Name	Behavior	Date	Action Taken	Parent Contact/Response

Room Inventory _____

Year ___ Grade ___ Teacher ___

G = good   **F** = fair   **P** = poor

Description	No.	Condition G F P	Comments	Description	No.	Condition G F P	Comments
Room furnishings:							
teacher desk							
teacher chair							
student desks							
student chairs							
tables				**Technological equipment:**			
pencil sharpeners				television			
trash cans				VCR			
shelves				overhead projector			
file cabinets				tape recorders			
other				headphones			
				computers			
				printers			
				computer accessories:			
Textbooks:							
math manuals				other			
math textbooks							
reading manuals							
reading textbooks							
language manuals				**Personal inventory:**			
language textbooks							
science manuals							
science textbooks							
social studies manuals							
social studies textbooks							
handwriting manuals							
other							

Instruction

Lesson plans for the week of _____

_____   _____
teacher   grade

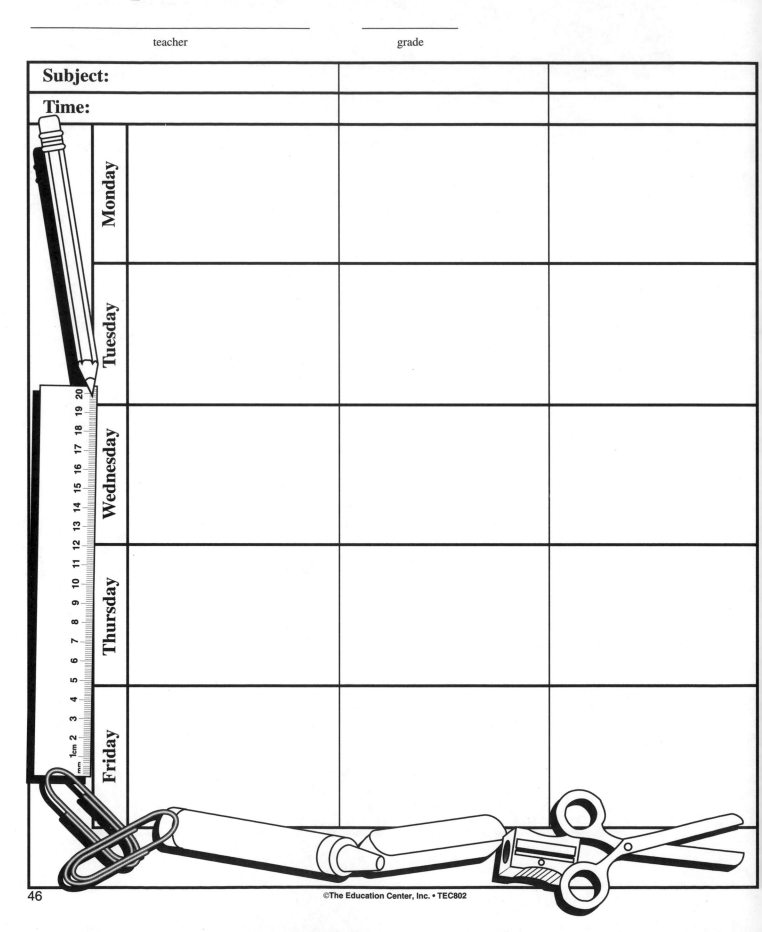

Subject:		
Time:		
Monday		
Tuesday		
Wednesday		
Thursday		
Friday		

©The Education Center, Inc. • TEC802

Duty: ☐ AM _____ ☐ Noon _____ ☐ PM _____

			Monday
			Tuesday
			Wednesday
			Thursday
			Friday

Lesson plans for the week of _____

_____   _____
teacher   grade

Subject:		
Time:		
Monday		
Tuesday		
Wednesday		
Thursday		
Friday		

Duty: ☐ AM _____ ☐ Noon _____ ☐ PM _____

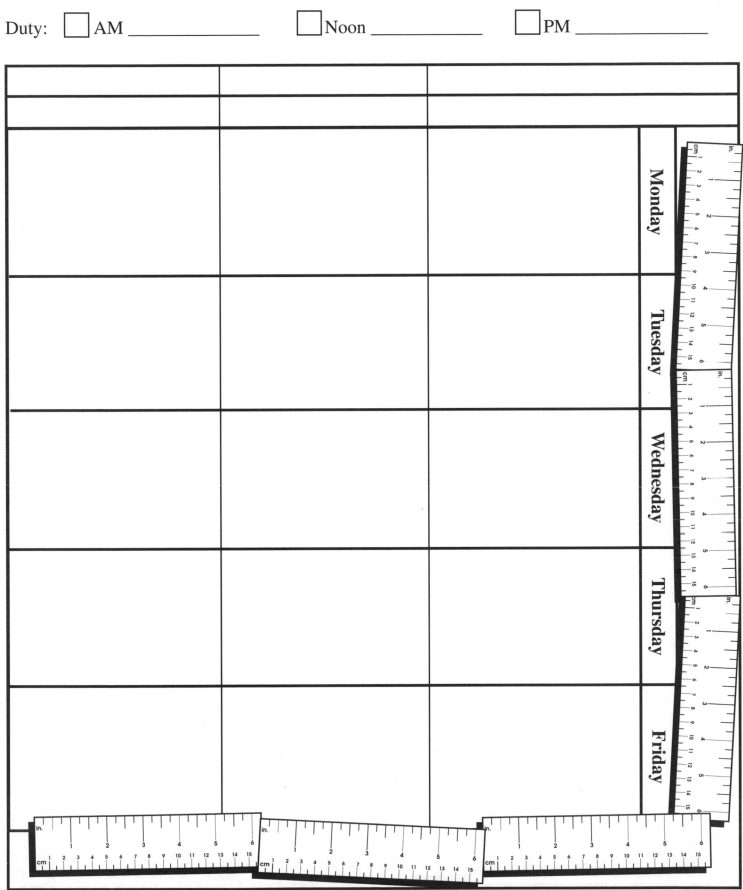

			Monday
			Tuesday
			Wednesday
			Thursday
			Friday

Lesson plans for _____

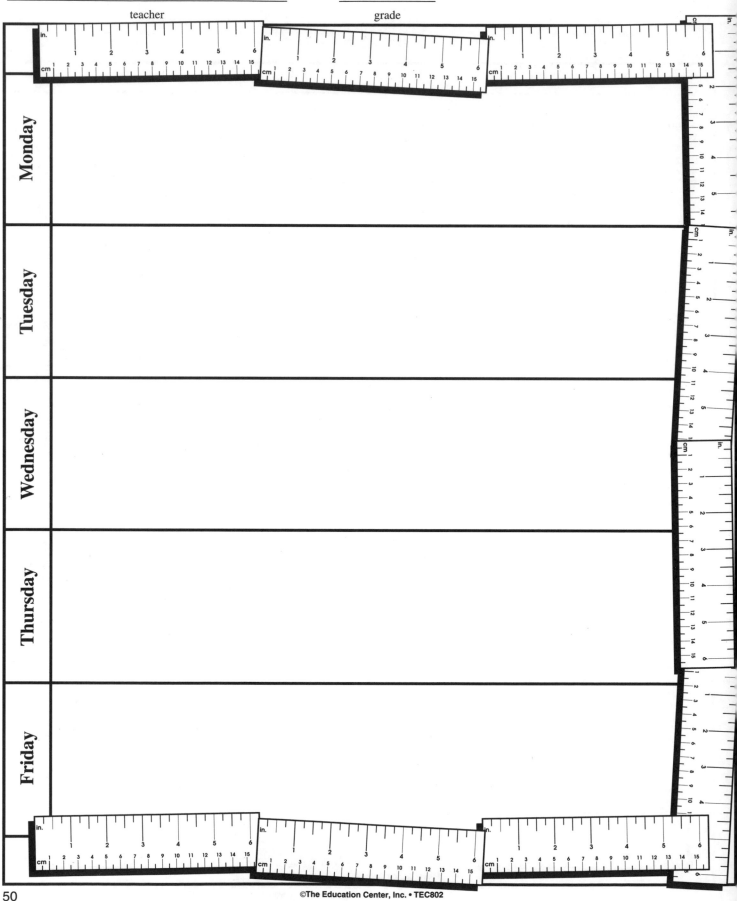

teacher _____   grade _____

Monday

Tuesday

Wednesday

Thursday

Friday

Thematic planner for...

theme

Reading

Resource	Description	Issue/Page(s)	Location

Language Arts

Resource	Description	Issue/Page(s)	Location

Social Studies

Resource	Description	Issue/Page(s)	Location

Science

Resource	Description	Issue/Page(s)	Location

Other

Resource	Description	Issue/Page(s)	Location

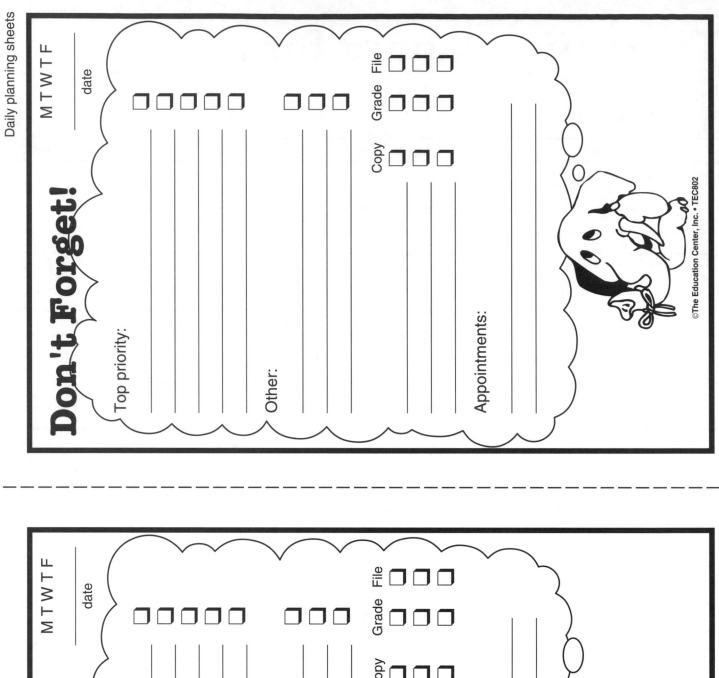

Don't Forget!

M T W T F

——————
date

☐☐☐☐☐

Top priority:
——————————————
——————————————
——————————————
——————————————

☐☐☐

Other:
——————————————
——————————————

Copy Grade File
☐   ☐   ☐
☐   ☐   ☐
☐   ☐   ☐

Appointments:
——————————————
——————————————

Don't Forget!

M T W T F

——————
date

☐☐☐☐☐

Top priority:
——————————————
——————————————
——————————————
——————————————

☐☐☐

Other:
——————————————
——————————————

Copy Grade File
☐   ☐   ☐
☐   ☐   ☐
☐   ☐   ☐

Appointments:
——————————————
——————————————

Grading Period: 1 2 3 4   **Subject** _____   **Period/Time** _____

Students	M	T	W	T	F	M	T	W	T	F	M	T	W	T	F	M	T	W	T	F	M	T	W	T	F	M	T	W	T	F	Final Average

Assignment descriptions:

Open chart

©The Education Center, Inc. • TEC802

name		score
subject		section

1. _____
2. _____
3. _____
4. _____
5. _____
6. _____
7. _____
8. _____
9. _____
10. _____
11. _____
12. _____
13. _____
14. _____
15. _____
16. _____
17. _____
18. _____
19. _____
20. _____
21. _____
22. _____
23. _____
24. _____
25. _____

name		score
subject		section

1. Ⓐ Ⓑ Ⓒ Ⓓ Ⓔ
2. Ⓐ Ⓑ Ⓒ Ⓓ Ⓔ
3. Ⓐ Ⓑ Ⓒ Ⓓ Ⓔ
4. Ⓐ Ⓑ Ⓒ Ⓓ Ⓔ
5. Ⓐ Ⓑ Ⓒ Ⓓ Ⓔ
6. Ⓐ Ⓑ Ⓒ Ⓓ Ⓔ
7. Ⓐ Ⓑ Ⓒ Ⓓ Ⓔ
8. Ⓐ Ⓑ Ⓒ Ⓓ Ⓔ
9. Ⓐ Ⓑ Ⓒ Ⓓ Ⓔ
10. Ⓐ Ⓑ Ⓒ Ⓓ Ⓔ
11. Ⓐ Ⓑ Ⓒ Ⓓ Ⓔ
12. Ⓐ Ⓑ Ⓒ Ⓓ Ⓔ
13. Ⓐ Ⓑ Ⓒ Ⓓ Ⓔ
14. Ⓐ Ⓑ Ⓒ Ⓓ Ⓔ
15. Ⓐ Ⓑ Ⓒ Ⓓ Ⓔ
16. Ⓐ Ⓑ Ⓒ Ⓓ Ⓔ
17. Ⓐ Ⓑ Ⓒ Ⓓ Ⓔ
18. Ⓐ Ⓑ Ⓒ Ⓓ Ⓔ
19. Ⓐ Ⓑ Ⓒ Ⓓ Ⓔ
20. Ⓐ Ⓑ Ⓒ Ⓓ Ⓔ
21. Ⓐ Ⓑ Ⓒ Ⓓ Ⓔ
22. Ⓐ Ⓑ Ⓒ Ⓓ Ⓔ
23. Ⓐ Ⓑ Ⓒ Ⓓ Ⓔ
24. Ⓐ Ⓑ Ⓒ Ⓓ Ⓔ
25. Ⓐ Ⓑ Ⓒ Ⓓ Ⓔ

Timed-Evaluation Progress Chart

_____   _____ – _____   _____
student name   from   to   subject

Activity/Skill	Time Given	Results/Comments

SUBSTITUTE FOLDER
for

_____ _____ _____
teacher   room no.   grade

Dear Substitute,
   The information in this folder should be helpful to you. Please write a note to me on the enclosed notepaper. I value your comments.

   Sincerely,

_____

©The Education Center, Inc. • TEC802

SUBSTITUTE FOLDER CHECKLIST

This folder contains:

❏ Class information

❏ Procedures

❏ Lesson plans

❏ School map

❏ Staff list

❏ Note paper

❏ _____

❏ _____

©The Education Center, Inc. • TEC802

Note To Teacher: Duplicate this page. Cut out the top and bottom sections of the page. Glue the cover to the front of a large file folder. Glue the checklist to the inside of the folder. Place substitute information inside the folder.

CLASS INFORMATION

_____   _____
teacher   grade

Student Name	Bus No.	Academic Needs	Medical Needs

PROCEDURES

Attendance	
Lunch Count/Milk Count	
Beginning Class	
Free Time	
Hall Traveling	
Behavior Problems/Discipline	
Fire Drill/Severe Weather	
Ending Class	

EMERGENCY LESSON PLANS

The lesson plan book is located _____

These activities are to be used: ☐ as a supplement only   ☐ at any time

	Description	Source	Location
Reading			
Language			
Math			
Science			
Social Studies			
Other			

SCHOOL MAP

Map Code

X = You are here.
① = Office
② = Faculty Rest Room
③ = Cafeteria
④ = Library
⑤ = _____

STAFF LIST

How to contact:

Principal _____ _____

Secretary _____ _____

Counselor _____ _____

Nurse _____ _____

Custodian _____ _____

Librarian _____ _____

Specialists (music, physical education, etc....):

Title

_____ _____ _____

_____ _____ _____

_____ _____ _____

_____ _____ _____

_____ _____ _____

_____ _____ _____

Teachers in this area:

grade/subject	teacher	room no./location
grade/subject	teacher	room no./location
grade/subject	teacher	room no./location
grade/subject	teacher	room no./location
grade/subject	teacher	room no./location

Notes: _____

_____

_____

Homework Kit

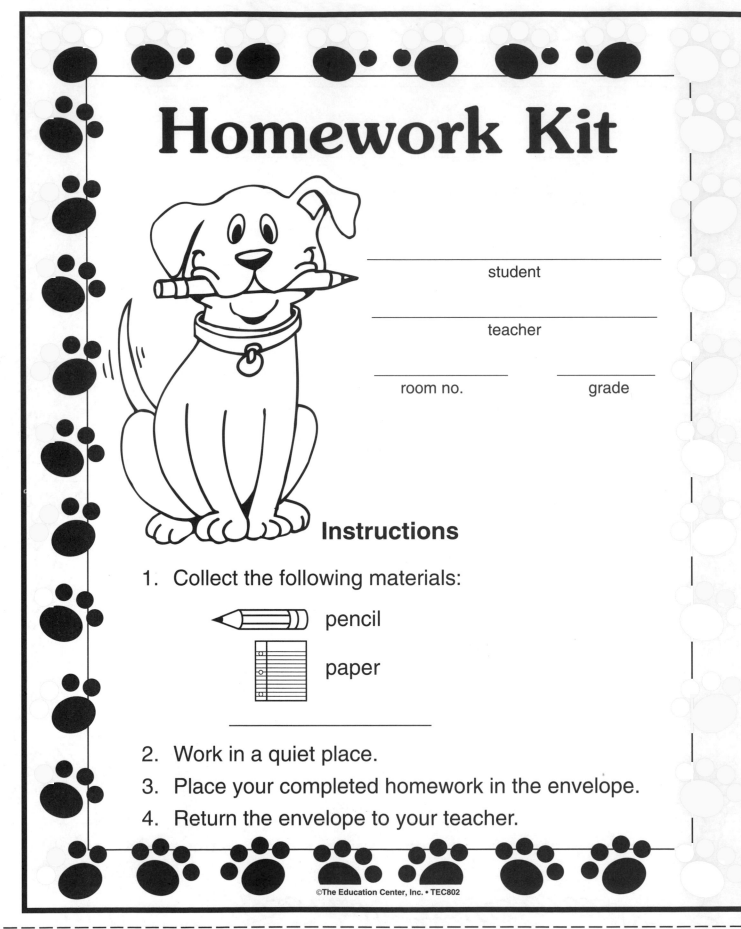

_____
student

_____
teacher

_____   _____
room no.   grade

Instructions

1. Collect the following materials:

   pencil

   paper

   _____

2. Work in a quiet place.
3. Place your completed homework in the envelope.
4. Return the envelope to your teacher.

©The Education Center, Inc. • TEC802

Note To Teacher: Duplicate this page for your students. Glue each page to the front of a large envelope. Place each student's homework inside an envelope along with a copy of the homework kit letter on page 66.

Homework Kit

_____
student

_____
teacher

_____   _____
room no.   grade

_____
subject

1. Choose the materials you need from the list below:

pencil	colored pencils	tape	_____
eraser	crayons	stapler	_____
paper	ruler	markers	_____
pen	scissors	calculator	_____

2. Work in a quiet place.

3. Complete each assignment before beginning another.

4. If you need help, review the directions; then _____

_____

_____

_____

©The Education Center, Inc. • TEC802

Note To Teacher: Duplicate this page for your students. Glue each page to the front of a large envelope. Place each student's homework inside an envelope along with a copy of the homework kit letter on page 67.

65

About The Homework Kit

Dear Parent,
    Your child's learning takes place in school and at home. You can help your child by stressing the importance of homework. By doing this work your child will:

❑ review skills

❑ practice skills in weak areas

❑ complete unfinished work

Your encouragement contributes to your child's success. Please return this kit on _____.

Sincerely,

_____

teacher signature

©The Education Center, Inc. • TEC802

About The Homework Kit

Dear Parent,
    Your child's learning takes place in school and at home. You can help your child by stressing the importance of homework. By doing this work your child will:

❑ review skills

❑ practice skills in weak areas

❑ complete unfinished work

Your encouragement contributes to your child's success. Please return this kit on _____.

Sincerely,

_____

teacher signature

©The Education Center, Inc. • TEC802

Note To Teacher: Duplicate the homework kit letter for each child. Complete each letter and place it in the child's homework kit (see page 64).

About The
Homework Kit

Dear Parent,
   The assignments in this homework kit are:

   ❏ for remedial help

   ❏ for review

   ❏ unfinished work

Please support your child in completing this homework. This kit should be returned by
_____. Thank you for your help!

Sincerely,

_____
teacher signature

©The Education Center, Inc. • TEC802

About The
Homework Kit

Dear Parent,
   The assignments in this homework kit are:

   ❏ for remedial help

   ❏ for review

   ❏ unfinished work

Please support your child in completing this homework. This kit should be returned by
_____. Thank you for your help!

Sincerely,

_____
teacher signature

©The Education Center, Inc. • TEC802

Note To Teacher: Duplicate the homework kit letter for each child. Complete each letter and place it in the child's homework kit (see page 65).

Homework Plan

Doing my homework is important.

This is my own plan.

_____

_____

_____

When my work is finished, my teacher will

_____

_____

_____

_____ student signature

Now, let's shake hands.

_____ teacher signature

We've made a plan!

Color a circle each day you follow your plan.

◯ Monday   ◯ Tuesday   ◯ Wednesday   ◯ Thursday   ◯ Friday

Homework Contract

For the week of _____

I, _____,

agree to this plan:

_____

_____

_____

_____

_____

I will turn in my work on _____

My reward for completing this contract will be _____

_____

_____   _____
student signature   teacher signature

Check a box each day you
follow your plan.

Monday ❑   Tuesday ❑

Wednesday ❑   Thursday ❑

Friday ❑

Reader/Leader
I will
- read clearly so that everyone in my group can hear.
- share the group's ideas with the class.
- keep the group working on the job.

©The Education Center, Inc. • TEC802

Checker/Helper
I will
- help people in my group.
- check my group's work.
- keep the group working on the job.

©The Education Center, Inc. • TEC802

Encourager
I will
- encourage others in the group.
- help others to do their best.
- keep the group working on the job.

©The Education Center, Inc. • TEC802

"Gopher"
I will
- go for help when it is needed.
- get the needed materials.
- keep the group working on the job.

©The Education Center, Inc. • TEC802

Writer
I will
- write or draw the group's ideas.
- be a good listener.
- keep the group working on the job.

©The Education Center, Inc. • TEC802

Leader

- guides the group by setting a good example
- helps all members participate
- keeps the group focused on the job

©The Education Center, Inc. • TEC802

Recorder

- listens closely to each member of the group
- writes down important information
- shares information with the class

©The Education Center, Inc. • TEC802

Encourager

- encourages others to be good listeners
- makes positive comments to group members
- supports others by helping

©The Education Center, Inc. • TEC802

Materials Manager

- gets needed materials for the group
- puts materials away
- delivers materials and messages

©The Education Center, Inc. • TEC802

Timekeeper

- notifies the group of the starting and stopping times
- helps keep the group on task
- keeps track of the remaining time and encourages the group to continue

©The Education Center, Inc. • TEC802

Cooperative-Group Planning Sheet

Cooperative learning focus: _____

Special instructions: _____
_____
_____

| 1. Reader/Leader | 2. Checker/Helper | 3. Encourager | 4. "Gopher" | 5. Writer |

Group _____
1. _____
2. _____
3. _____
4. _____
5. _____

Group _____
1. _____
2. _____
3. _____
4. _____
5. _____

Group _____
1. _____
2. _____
3. _____
4. _____
5. _____

Group _____
1. _____
2. _____
3. _____
4. _____
5. _____

Comments: _____
_____
_____

Cooperative-Group Planning Sheet

Cooperative learning focus: _____

Subject: _____   Date: _____

Special Instructions: _____   Period: _____

1. Leader   2. Recorder   3. Encourager   4. Materials Manager   5. Timekeeper

Group _____

1. _____
2. _____
3. _____
4. _____
5. _____

Group _____

1. _____
2. _____
3. _____
4. _____
5. _____

Group _____

1. _____
2. _____
3. _____
4. _____
5. _____

Group _____

1. _____
2. _____
3. _____
4. _____
5. _____

Comments: _____

Cooperative-Learning Progress Chart

Date

Task:						
Group						
Group						
Group						
Group						
Group						
Group						

name

teacher date

**Punch a hole after each
completed activity.**

©The Education Center, Inc. • TEC802

---

name

teacher date

**Punch a hole after each
completed activity.**

©The Education Center, Inc. • TEC802

---

name

teacher date

**Punch a hole after each
completed activity.**

©The Education Center, Inc. • TEC802

Note To Teacher: Duplicate one copy of this page and program the necessary information. Then duplicate copies and cut them apart for your students. As each child completes an activity, have him use a hole puncher to punch a hole in the circle next to the activity.

Special Needs Chart

_____ subject

_____ date

_____ student

_____ teacher   _____ grade

Skill	Activity	Reteach	Reinforce	Recheck

Name _____

Work Watcher

How did you do on _____?

Color a face to answer each question.

1. Did I listen?   ☺ 😐 ☹
2. Did I work quietly?   ☺ 😐 ☹
3. Did I do my best?   ☺ 😐 ☹
4. Am I proud of my work?   ☺ 😐 ☹
5. Did I enjoy my work?   ☺ 😐 ☹

Next time I will _____

_____

Name _____

Work Watcher

How did you do on _____?

Color a face to answer each question.

1. Did I listen?   ☺ 😐 ☹
2. Did I work quietly?   ☺ 😐 ☹
3. Did I do my best?   ☺ 😐 ☹
4. Am I proud of my work?   ☺ 😐 ☹
5. Did I enjoy my work?   ☺ 😐 ☹

Next time I will _____

_____

Name _____

The Way I See It

This is an evaluation of _____.
                                      activity

Circle the numbers that best describe your work.

	Good	Fair	Poor
1. I completed my work.	3	2	1
2. I prepared well ahead of time.	3	2	1
3. I used my time wisely.	3	2	1
4. I cooperated with others.	3	2	1
5. I checked my grammar, punctuation, and spelling.	3	2	1
6. I followed directions.	3	2	1
7. I did my best.	3	2	1
8. I am satisfied with my work.	3	2	1

Add the numbers in each column.
Write each total in the box below the column.
Add the numbers in the boxes to find your total score.

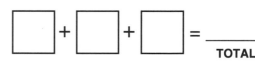

☐ + ☐ + ☐ = _____
                        TOTAL

The way I see it, you are a winner as you improve your score!

Complete the sentence.

If I could do this assignment again, I would _____

_____

_____

78

My Portfolio

Name

Portfolio Assessment Record

for _____
student

The intended audience for this collection is

❑   student and teacher   ❑   teacher and parent   ❑   the public

Entry description	Skill mastery observation	Conferences 1st	2nd	Comments on the degree of success

Name _____

Let's Talk About It!

_____
date

What activity are you working on now? _____

_____

Circle your answers.

My work is	finished.	not finished.	
This work is	my best.	okay.	not my best.
This work is	easy.	just right.	difficult.

I'm glad we talked about it!

Complete the sentences.

Next, I plan to _____

_____

_____

My teacher says _____

_____

_____

_____   _____
student signature   teacher signature

Place this report in your portfolio.

Name _____   Date _____

My Conference Report

Assignment: _____

Progress: ❑ beginning   ❑ in progress   ❑ completed

I like the way I _____

_____

_____

I need to correct _____

_____

My next step is _____

_____

_____

I will share my work by _____

_____

My special comment: _____

_____

_____

My teacher's special comment: _____

_____

_____

_____   _____
student signature   teacher signature

Place this report in your portfolio.

©The Education Center, Inc. • TEC802

All About _____
name

This is me.

This is my family.

This is how I feel about

—school.

—reading.

—watching TV.

—playing with friends.

—learning new things.

—me.

The things I like are _____

_____

The things I do not like are _____

_____

I am good at _____

_____

I wish I could _____

_____

Introducing _____
name

Complete the sentences.

1. My favorite subjects are _____
_____

2. My hobbies are _____
_____

3. After school I _____
_____

4. I wish I could _____
_____

5. I would like to meet _____
_____

6. Sometimes I am _____
_____

7. When I am older _____
_____

8. My family is _____
_____

9. I would like to visit _____

10. The most important thing to me is _____

11. I am happy when _____

12. I do not like _____

13. A great thing about me is _____
_____

_____
name

Each day, I have
something to say.

_____

_____

_____

_____

_____

_____

_____

_____

_____

_____

_____

_____

_____

Journal Writing

_____
name

My thoughts are like clouds…they come and they go.

Date: _____

Date: _____

Date: _____

Reading Contract

_____   _____
student   date

I agree to read:

_____
book title

I will read _____ pages each day.

When I am finished, I will share the story by

_____   telling about it.

_____   writing about it.

_____   drawing a picture.

_____   other _____

_____   _____
student signature   teacher signature

©The Education Center, Inc. • TEC802

- -

Reading Contract

_____   _____
student   date

I agree to read:

_____
book title

I will read _____ pages each day.

When I am finished, I will share the story by

_____   telling about it.

_____   writing about it.

_____   drawing a picture.

_____   other _____

_____   _____
student signature   teacher signature

©The Education Center, Inc. • TEC802

Reading Contract

_____
date

I, _____, agree to read _____.
student   number of books or pages

To do this I will need to read _____ each day.
                                                    pages or minutes

I plan to complete this contract in _____.
                                                          number of days or weeks

I will keep a record of my progress.

_____
student signature

_____
teacher signature

©The Education Center, Inc. • TEC802

Reading Contract

_____
date

I, _____, agree to read _____.
student   number of books or pages

To do this I will need to read _____ each day.
                                                    pages or minutes

I plan to complete this contract in _____.
                                                          number of days or weeks

I will keep a record of my progress.

_____
student signature

_____
teacher signature

©The Education Center, Inc. • TEC802

Reading Group Chart

Group _____   Text _____

_____
date

Students	Skills										Comments
1.										
2.										
3.										
4.										
5.										
6.										
7.										
8.										

©The Education Center, Inc. • TEC802

Reading Group Chart

Group _____   Text _____

_____
date

Students	Skills										Comments
1.										
2.										
3.										
4.										
5.										
6.										
7.										
8.										

©The Education Center, Inc. • TEC802

At-Home Reading

_____ read
child

_____ pages/minutes today. I am so proud of my child!

_____   _____
date   parent signature

At-Home Reading

_____ read
child

_____ pages/minutes today. I am so proud of my child!

_____   _____
date   parent signature

At-Home Reading

_____ read
child

_____ pages/minutes today. I am so proud of my child!

_____   _____
date   parent signature

At-Home Reading

_____ read
child

_____ pages/minutes today. I am so proud of my child!

_____   _____
date   parent signature

Reading Verification

I verify that my child, _____,

read the following:

_____   _____

title of material   pages/minutes

_____   _____

date   parent signature

©The Education Center, Inc. • TEC802

Reading Verification

I verify that my child, _____,

read the following:

_____   _____

title of material   pages/minutes

_____   _____

date   parent signature

©The Education Center, Inc. • TEC802

Reading Verification

I verify that my child, _____,

read the following:

_____   _____

title of material   pages/minutes

_____   _____

date   parent signature

©The Education Center, Inc. • TEC802

Reading Verification

I verify that my child, _____,

read the following:

_____   _____

title of material   pages/minutes

_____   _____

date   parent signature

©The Education Center, Inc. • TEC802

Name _____

I Read At Home

Day	Today I read	I read to
Monday		
Tuesday		
Wednesday		
Thursday		
Friday		
Saturday		
Sunday		

©The Education Center, Inc. • TEC802

Name _____

I Read At Home

Day	Today I read	I read to
Monday		
Tuesday		
Wednesday		
Thursday		
Friday		
Saturday		
Sunday		

©The Education Center, Inc. • TEC802

Name _____

Home Reading Record

Date	Title (or type of material read)	Minutes	Pages	Parent Initials

Reading Is Fun!

The name of my book is _____

It was written by _____

The book was about _____
_____

My favorite part was _____
_____

Book rating: (circle one)

E for excellent

S for satisfactory

N for needs improvement

Book Report

Title: _____

Author: _____

Type of book: _____   Number of pages: _____

Write a summary of the book.

_____

_____

_____

_____

_____

_____

What would you like to change about this book?_____

_____

_____

Write five interesting words from the book.
Use your dictionary to find the definition of each word.
Write the definitions on the lines.

1. _____

_____

2. _____

_____

3. _____

_____

4. _____

_____

5. _____

_____

Research Contract
for

_____
student

I will learn more about _____.
I will look in books, encyclopedias, and magazines.
I will share what I learn with my class by

_____ drawing a picture.
_____ telling about it.
_____ writing about it.
_____ other _____
I will evaluate my work with my teacher.

_____
today's date

_____
student signature

_____
date completed

_____
teacher signature

©The Education Center, Inc. • TEC802

Research Contract
for

_____
student

I will learn more about _____.
I will look in books, encyclopedias, and magazines.
I will share what I learn with my class by

_____ drawing a picture.
_____ telling about it.
_____ writing about it.
_____ other _____
I will evaluate my work with my teacher.

_____
today's date

_____
student signature

_____
date completed

_____
teacher signature

©The Education Center, Inc. • TEC802

Research Contract

Topic: _____

Write the number of items you will use of each of these sources:

____ encyclopedia   ____ television program

____ dictionary   ____ radio program

____ almanac   ____ interview

____ atlas   ____ newspaper

____ nonfiction book   ____ pamphlet

____ magazine   other

____ reference book   ____ _____

____ textbook   ____ _____

____ video

I will share my project by:

____ writing a report

____ giving an oral report

____ making a _____

I will add interest to my project by _____

_____

_____

_____

I will discuss my work with my teacher as I research and prepare my project. My project will be completed by _____.

                                                                  date

_____   _____

      student signature   date

_____

      teacher signature

Name _____

Research Planner

1. I am going to learn about _____
2. Here are some things I already know about my topic. _____

   _____

   _____

   _____

3. Here are three things I'd like to learn about my topic.

   _____

   _____

   _____

4. I will use these sources:

   _____

   _____

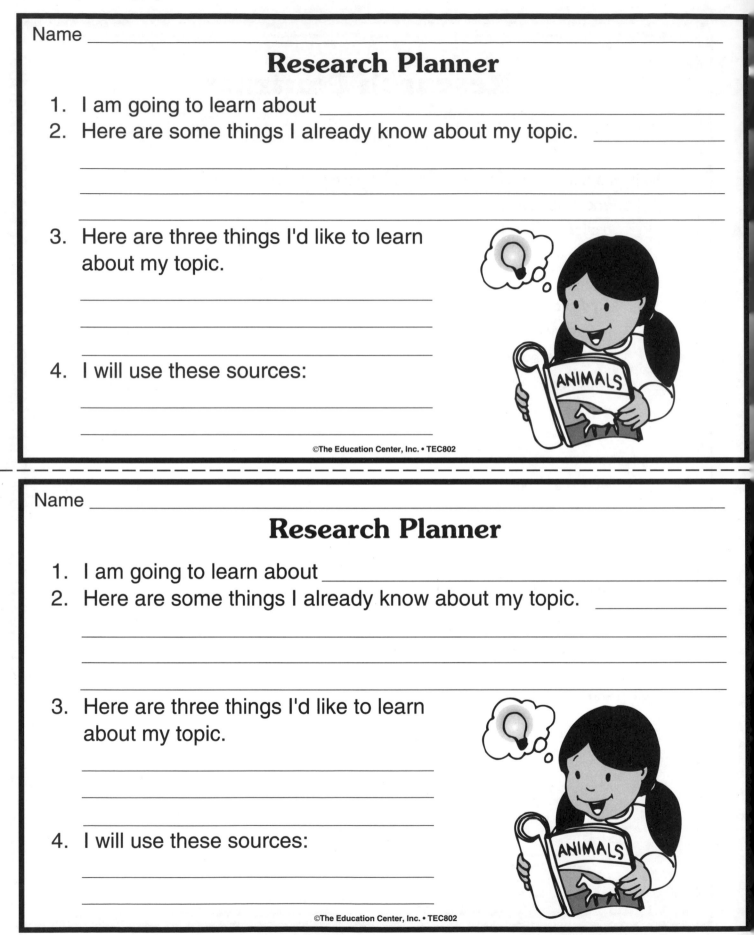

©The Education Center, Inc. • TEC802

Name _____

Research Planner

1. I am going to learn about _____
2. Here are some things I already know about my topic. _____

   _____

   _____

   _____

3. Here are three things I'd like to learn about my topic.

   _____

   _____

   _____

4. I will use these sources:

   _____

   _____

©The Education Center, Inc. • TEC802

Research Planner

Topic: _____ Date: _____

List information that you already know about your topic.

_____

_____

_____

_____

_____

In each section below, write a question you would like to answer through
   your research.

Write your notes on the lines below each question.

List each source, author, and page number.

1. _____ ?

   Notes: _____

_____

_____

   Source: _____ Author: _____ Page(s): _____

2. _____ ?

   Notes: _____

_____

_____

   Source: _____ Author: _____ Page(s): _____

3. _____ ?

   Notes: _____

_____

_____

   Source: _____ Author: _____ Page(s): _____

4. _____ ?

   Notes: _____

_____

_____

   Source: _____ Author: _____ Page(s): _____

_____
date

Science Lab Guide

Group members:

_____

_____

_____

_____

_____

Assignment: _____

Here is what we will do.	Color when completed.
Get the materials we need.	
Read the instructions carefully.	
Do the experiment.	
Talk about what happened.	
Write about what happened.	
Talk about why we think it happened.	
Write about why we think it happened.	
Put the materials away.	
Other:	

Note To Teacher: Duplicate one copy of this page for each group. Have students use the steps on the page to guide them through their cooperative science activities.

Science Lab Report

Group members: _____   _____

_____   _____

Assignment: _____

Materials needed: _____

_____

Procedure: _____

_____

_____

_____

_____

_____

Results: _____

_____

_____

_____

_____

_____

Conclusion: _____

_____

_____

_____

_____

Name _____

Lab Chart

Write the names of your group members on the ice blocks.

_____
name

_____
name

_____
name

_____
name

_____
name

_____
name

_____
name

_____
name

_____
name

Gather the materials below.
Sit with your group.

_____   _____   _____

_____   _____   _____

_____   _____   _____

Read the directions below.
Draw an X on a snowball when you finish the job.

○ _____

○ _____

○ _____

○ _____

○ _____

Note To Teacher: Duplicate one copy of this page. Program the page with the necessary materials and directions. Then duplicate a copy for each child in your class.

Science Fair Entry Form

Name: _____ Grade:_____

School: _____

Teacher: _____

Project title: _____

Do you need an electrical outlet? _____

> I certify that this exhibit is entirely my own work.
>
> _____
> exhibitor signature

Please return this form to _____ by _____.

©The Education Center, Inc. • TEC802

Science Fair Entry Form

Name: _____ Grade:_____

School: _____

Teacher: _____

Project title: _____

Do you need an electrical outlet? _____

> I certify that this exhibit is entirely my own work.
>
> _____
> exhibitor signature

Please return this form to _____ by _____.

©The Education Center, Inc. • TEC802

Name _____

Science Project Planner

1. Choose a topic.
   I want to learn more about _____

2. State your question.

   _____ does _____
   (what, why, how, when, where)

   _____?

3. Form a hypothesis.
   I think _____

   _____

4. Plan the steps of your experiment.

   a. _____

   b. _____

   c. _____

   d. _____

   e. _____

   f. _____

   g. _____

   h. _____

5. Gather your materials and references.
   I will need _____

   _____

6. After conducting the experiment, record your results.
   I will record the information by _____

   _____

   _____

On the back of this sheet, draw a picture of what you
think your project will look like.

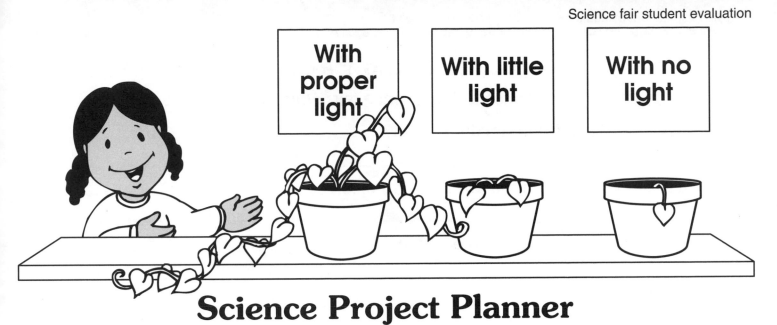

Science Project Planner

Think about what you have seen and learned from your experience at the science fair. Complete this chart.

	Yes	Somewhat	No
1. I was satisfied with my project.	❑	❑	❑
2. I received help from others when I had questions.	❑	❑	❑
3. I was able to find materials easily.	❑	❑	❑
4. My teachers and parents encouraged me.	❑	❑	❑
5. I had a plan to follow.	❑	❑	❑
6. I allowed enough time to complete my project.	❑	❑	❑
7. I did my best work.	❑	❑	❑
8. I understood how to set up my project at the fair.	❑	❑	❑
9. I was prepared for the judges.	❑	❑	❑
10. I would like to enter another fair.	❑	❑	❑
11. I learned many new things at the fair.	❑	❑	❑

_____   _____
            name   date

Looking Back

Think about your experience at the science fair. Write your thoughts below.

1. What did you like about your project?_____

_____

2. What would you change about your project?_____

_____

3. What was your favorite project at the fair?_____

_____

Why?_____

_____

4. What would you change about the science fair?_____

_____

5. Additional comments: _____

_____   _____
name   date

©The Education Center, Inc. • TEC802

Looking Back

Think about your experience at the science fair. Write your thoughts below.

1. What did you like about your project?_____

_____

2. What would you change about your project?_____

_____

3. What was your favorite project at the fair?_____

_____

Why?_____

_____

4. What would you change about the science fair?_____

_____

5. Additional comments: _____

_____   _____
name   date

©The Education Center, Inc. • TEC802

Communications

School Supplies

Dear Parent,

Danny needs

the following school supplies:

✓	pencils	☑ No. 2	❑ red	
✓	pens	☑ black	❑ blue	❑ red
✓	markers	☑ all colors	❑ _____	
___	colored pencils			
___	crayons			
___	notebook paper	❑ wide rul		
		❑		
___	3-ring noteb			
___	Spi			

Injury Report

March 25, 1993
date

was

Dear Parent,
This is to report that _Hayley_ stud
injured at school.

Injury: _scraped knee_

Treatment: _alcohol and b_

Treated by: _nurse_

Follow-up suggestions: _____

Please sign and return this notic

_____
parent signature

We're Going On A Field Trip!

Field trip form (Pri.)

Dear Parent,
We are planning a trip to

the zoo

on _Friday_, _May 3, 1993_. Your child will

bring:

• field trip permission form (below)
• _sack lunch_
• _drink_
• _____

Keep this note and post it at home as a reminder. Thank you.

- - - - - - - Cut here and return the form below. - - - - - - -

Miss Kelly
teacher signature

the field trip to _____ has my permission to go on
scheduled on _____,

_____
parent signature

_____
date

Dear _____,

Welcome to the _____ grade! I am excited about having you in my class.

Our school day begins at _____. This year we will be
time
learning about _____

_____

_____

_____

Here are some things you may bring to school:

_____

_____

_____

I am anxious to learn more about you and the things you enjoy.

Your teacher,

_____

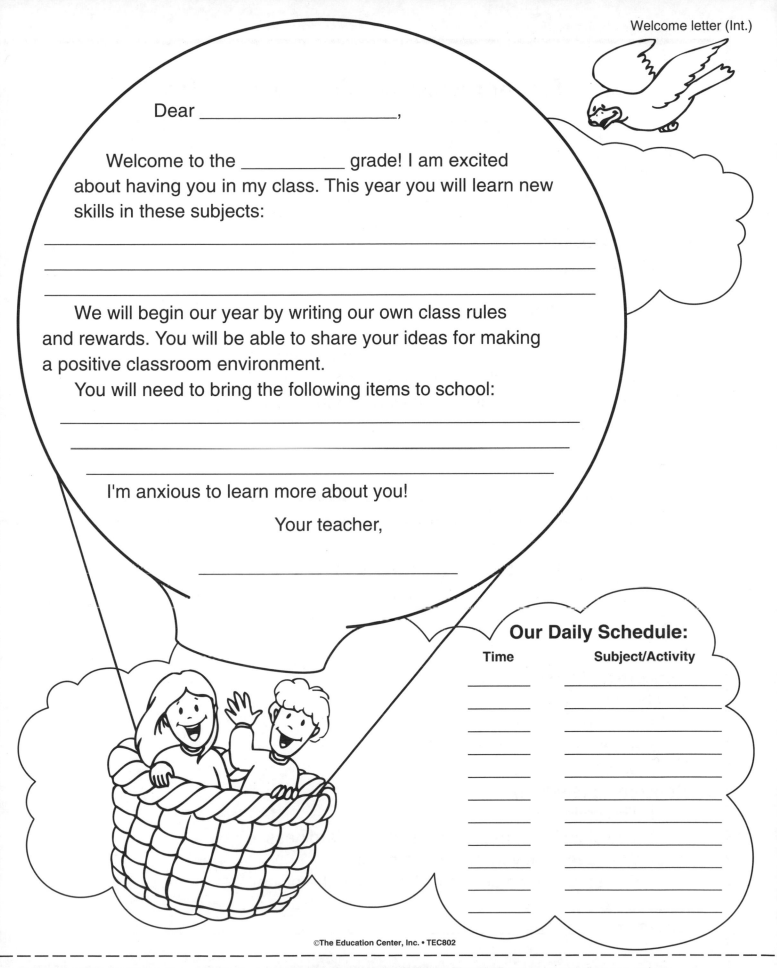

Dear _____,

Welcome to the _____ grade! I am excited about having you in my class. This year you will learn new skills in these subjects:

_____
_____
_____

We will begin our year by writing our own class rules and rewards. You will be able to share your ideas for making a positive classroom environment.

You will need to bring the following items to school:

_____
_____
_____

I'm anxious to learn more about you!

Your teacher,

_____

Our Daily Schedule:

Time   Subject/Activity

Note To Teacher: Duplicate one copy of this page and program the necessary information. Then duplicate copies to mail to your students before the school year begins.

Teacher Message From The Office

_____ M T W T F _____ AM PM
date   time

To: _____

From: _____

Concerning (personal): _____

You have:
- ❏ an appointment
- ❏ a delivery
- ❏ other

Concerning (student): _____
- ❏ The child is ill.
- ❏ The child is excused for absence or tardiness.
- ❏ We have received the child's records.
- ❏ Please send the child's homework to the office.
- ❏ Other _____

Comments: _____

©The Education Center, Inc. • TEC802

Teacher Message From The Office

_____ M T W T F _____ AM PM
date   time

To: _____

From: _____

Concerning (personal): _____

You have:
- ❏ an appointment
- ❏ a delivery
- ❏ other

Concerning (student): _____
- ❏ The child is ill.
- ❏ The child is excused for absence or tardiness.
- ❏ We have received the child's records.
- ❏ Please send the child's homework to the office.
- ❏ Other _____

Comments: _____

©The Education Center, Inc. • TEC802

Student Message From The Office

_____   _____ M T W T F_____
            teacher   date   time

To:_____

From: ❑ parent ❑ other _____

Message:

❑ Ride the bus   ❑ home.   ❑ to _____

❑ Walk   ❑ home.   ❑ to _____

❑ You will be picked up by ❑ parent.   ❑ other _____

❑ You have a delivery in the office.

Comments: _____

_____

_____

_____

©The Education Center, Inc. • TEC802

Student Message From The Office

_____   _____ M T W T F_____
            teacher   date   time

To:_____

From: ❑ parent ❑ other _____

Message:

❑ Ride the bus   ❑ home.   ❑ to _____

❑ Walk   ❑ home.   ❑ to _____

❑ You will be picked up by ❑ parent.   ❑ other _____

❑ You have a delivery in the office.

Comments: _____

_____

_____

_____

©The Education Center, Inc. • TEC802

Teacher Assistant Request

_____ M T W T F_____

date   time

To: _____

From: _____

Concerning: _____

Please

❏ call _____ about _____

number

❏ send to _____

❏ make copies.   No. of copies: _____   ❏ one side   ❏ both sides

❏ type.

❏ make a ditto or thermofax master.

❏ make a transparency.

❏ other _____

Comments: _____

_____

©The Education Center, Inc. • TEC802

Teacher Assistant Request

_____ M T W T F_____

date   time

To: _____

From: _____

Concerning: _____

Please

❏ call _____ about _____

number

❏ send to _____

❏ make copies.   No. of copies: _____   ❏ one side   ❏ both sides

❏ type.

❏ make a ditto or thermofax master.

❏ make a transparency.

❏ other _____

Comments: _____

_____

©The Education Center, Inc. • TEC802

Midterm Progress Report
Grading Period 1 2 3 4 _____
date

Dear Parent,

    This progress report is an informal evaluation of your child's progress for the first half of this grading period. Please discuss this report with your child.

The overall quality of_____'s work has been
- ❑ commendable.
- ❑ an improvement.
- ❑ below the regular performance.
- ❑ unsatisfactory in some areas.

Classwork has been
- ❑ Excellent
- ❑ Satisfactory
- ❑ Unsatisfactory in

_____

Test performance has been
- ❑ Excellent
- ❑ Satisfactory
- ❑ Unsatisfactory in

_____

A conference is   ❑ not necessary. ❑ requested. Please call.

Teacher comment: _____

_____

_____
teacher signature

Parent comment: _____

_____

_____
parent signature

Please sign and return.

Weekly Progress Report

_____
student name

_____
date

Work Habits
- ☐ Works independently and completes work
- ☐ Needs some assistance
- ☐ Needs a great deal of assistance
- ☐ Is easily distracted

Behavior
- ☐ Demonstrates self-control
- ☐ Demonstrates improving behavior
- ☐ Does not demonstrate self-control

Effort/Attitude
- ☐ Excellent
- ☐ Good
- ☐ Average
- ☐ Needs improvement

_____
teacher signature

_____
parent signature

- ☐ If checked, please sign and return.

©The Education Center, Inc. • TEC802

Weekly Progress Report

_____
student name

_____
date

Work Habits
- ☐ Works independently and completes work
- ☐ Needs some assistance
- ☐ Needs a great deal of assistance
- ☐ Is easily distracted

Behavior
- ☐ Demonstrates self-control
- ☐ Demonstrates improving behavior
- ☐ Does not demonstrate self-control

Effort/Attitude
- ☐ Excellent
- ☐ Good
- ☐ Average
- ☐ Needs improvement

_____
teacher signature

_____
parent signature

- ☐ If checked, please sign and return.

©The Education Center, Inc. • TEC802

Weekly Progress Report

_____   _____
student name   date

Your child is showing progress by

- ☐ an improved attitude.
- ☐ improved effort.
- ☐ maintaining a passing grade average.
- ☐ an improved grade average.
- ☐ completing work.
- ☐ using time wisely.

Difficulties are attributed to

- ☐ frequent absences.
- ☐ poor work habits.
- ☐ low skill level in _____
- ☐ other _____

Suggestions:

_____
_____
_____
_____

_____
teacher signature

_____
parent signature

☐ If checked, please sign and return.

©The Education Center, Inc. • TEC802

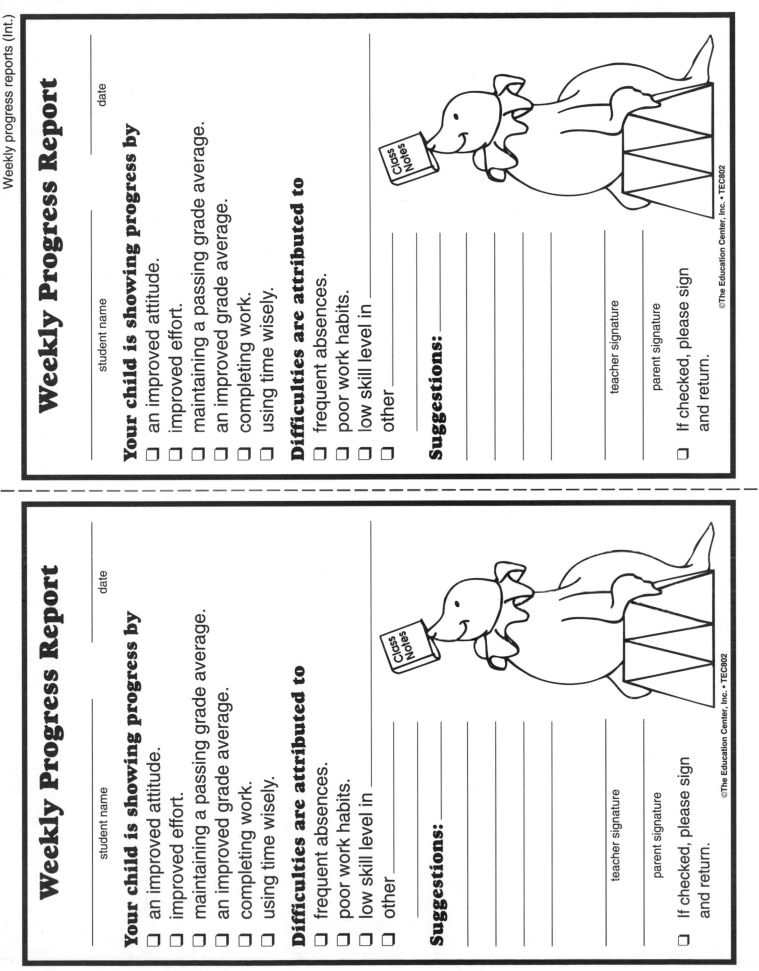

Weekly Progress Report

_____   _____
student name   date

Your child is showing progress by

- ☐ an improved attitude.
- ☐ improved effort.
- ☐ maintaining a passing grade average.
- ☐ an improved grade average.
- ☐ completing work.
- ☐ using time wisely.

Difficulties are attributed to

- ☐ frequent absences.
- ☐ poor work habits.
- ☐ low skill level in _____
- ☐ other _____

Suggestions:

_____
_____
_____
_____

_____
teacher signature

_____
parent signature

☐ If checked, please sign and return.

©The Education Center, Inc. • TEC802

Current Grade Report

_____ _____
student name   date

Dear Parent,

Your child is currently performing at the levels marked below.

E = Excellent   S = Satisfactory   N = Needs improvement

Comments

____ Reading   _____
____ Spelling   _____
____ Language   _____
____ Math   _____
____ Science   _____
____ Social Studies _____
____ other   _____
____ other   _____

Suggestions: _____

_____

Parent comment: _____

Please sign and return.

_____
teacher signature

_____
parent signature

©The Education Center, Inc. • TEC802

Current Grade Report

_____ _____
student name   date

Dear Parent,

Your child is currently performing at the levels marked below.

E = Excellent   S = Satisfactory   N = Needs improvement

Comments

____ Reading   _____
____ Spelling   _____
____ Language   _____
____ Math   _____
____ Science   _____
____ Social Studies _____
____ other   _____
____ other   _____

Suggestions: _____

_____

Parent comment: _____

Please sign and return.

_____
teacher signature

©The Education Center, Inc. • TEC802

Current Grade Average Report

_____ _____
student name   date

Dear Parent,

The current grade averages for your child are:

                                          Comments

____ Reading   _____
____ Spelling   _____
____ Language   _____
____ Math   _____
____ Science   _____
____ Social Studies   _____
____ other   _____
____ other   _____

Suggestions: _____
_____

_____
teacher signature

Parent comment: _____
_____

Please sign and return.

Current Grade Average Report

_____ _____
student name   date

Dear Parent,

The current grade averages for your child are:

                                          Comments

____ Reading   _____
____ Spelling   _____
____ Language   _____
____ Math   _____
____ Science   _____
____ Social Studies   _____
____ other   _____
____ other   _____

Suggestions: _____
_____

_____
teacher signature

Parent comment: _____
_____

Please sign and return.

_____
parent signature

Absence and Tardy Report _____
date

Dear Parent,

Our records show that _____ has a significant number of absences or tardies.
student

Absent _____ times during _____.
period or days

Tardy _____ times during _____.
period or days

Regular and prompt attendance is vital to your child's success in school. We value your support and request your help in improving your child's attendance record.

Thank you for your help.

Sincerely,

_____
teacher signature

Please sign and return the portion below.

- -

I have received the Absence and Tardy Report for my child.

_____   _____
child's name   parent signature

_____   _____
teacher signature   date

Comment: _____

©The Education Center, Inc. • TEC802

Absence and Tardy Report _____
date

Dear Parent,

Our records show that _____ has a significant number of absences or tardies.
student

Absent _____ times during _____.
period or days

Tardy _____ times during _____.
period or days

Regular and prompt attendance is vital to your child's success in school. We value your support and request your help in improving your child's attendance record.

Thank you for your help.

Sincerely,

_____
teacher signature

Please sign and return the portion below.

- -

I have received the Absence and Tardy Report for my child.

_____   _____
child's name   parent signature

_____   _____
teacher signature   date

Comment: _____

©The Education Center, Inc. • TEC802

Dear Parent,

    Your conference for _____
has been scheduled at _____
on _____, _____.

    Please complete the bottom portion of this form and
return it to me as soon as possible.
    I look forward to visiting with you.

Sincerely,

_____
teacher signature

❑ I plan to attend my child's conference at the scheduled time.
❑ I will need to reschedule our conference.

_____   _____
child's name   parent signature

©The Education Center, Inc. • TEC802

Dear Parent,

    Your conference for _____
has been scheduled at _____
on _____, _____.

    Please complete the bottom portion of this form and
return it to me as soon as possible.
    I look forward to visiting with you.

Sincerely,

_____
teacher signature

❑ I plan to attend my child's conference at the scheduled time.
❑ I will need to reschedule our conference.

_____   _____
child's name   parent signature

©The Education Center, Inc. • TEC802

Preconference questionnaire

Dear Parent,

I am looking forward to meeting with you at our parent-teacher conference. In preparing for our visit, I would like to know more about your child and your areas of concern.

Please answer the questions below and return the form to me as soon as possible. These insights to your child will help us make the best use of our time together. Thank you for your help!

Sincerely,

_____
teacher signature

Cut off and return the bottom portion.

- -

Child's name _____

My child's interests are _____

_____

My child's out-of-school activities include _____

_____

My child learns best by _____

_____

My child's attitude toward school is _____

_____

Topics I am most concerned about include:

___ work habits at school	___ listening/attention
___ study habits at home	___ respect for others
___ attitude	___ skill level in _____
___ self-control	_____
___ relations with friends	___ other _____
___ self-esteem	___ other _____

Comments: _____

_____

_____

_____   _____
parent signature   date

Conference Schedule

_____
conference date

_____
teacher

7:30 _____

7:45 _____

8:00 _____

8:15 _____

8:30 _____

8:45 _____

9:00 _____

9:15 _____

9:30 _____

9:45 _____

10:00 _____

10:15 _____

10:30 _____

10:45 _____

11:00 _____

11:15 _____

11:30 _____

11:45 _____

12:00 _____

12:15 _____

12:30 _____

12:45 _____

1:00 _____

1:15 _____

1:30 _____

1:45 _____

2:00 _____

2:15 _____

2:30 _____

2:45 _____

3:00 _____

3:15 _____

3:30 _____

3:45 _____

4:00 _____

ADDITIONAL CONFERENCES

_____

_____

_____

_____

_____

_____

_____

_____

_____

_____

Parent/Teacher Conference Report

Fall/Spring Conference of _____
date

Student: _____
Grade: _____
Teacher: _____

SUBJECTS

	Progress				Effort			
	Excellent	Satisfactory	Needs Improvement	Unsatisfactory	Excellent	Satisfactory	Needs Improvement	Unsatisfactory
Reading								
Math								
Language								
Penmanship								
Spelling								
Science								
Social Studies								
Other:								

SPECIAL SUBJECTS

	Progress				Effort			
Art								
Music								
Library								
Computer								
P.E.								
Other:								

WORK HABITS

	Excellent	Satisfactory	Needs Improvement	Unsatisfactory
Listens				
Follows directions				
Works independently				
Works accurately				
Works neatly				
Completes work on time				

ATTITUDES

	Excellent	Satisfactory	Needs Improvement	Unsatisfactory
Gets along with others				
Is courteous and cooperates				
Demonstrates self-control				
Shows respect for others				
Cares for personal property				
Assumes responsibility for actions				

Days absent: _____ Days tardy: _____

Comments: _____

Teacher signature: _____

Parent signature: _____

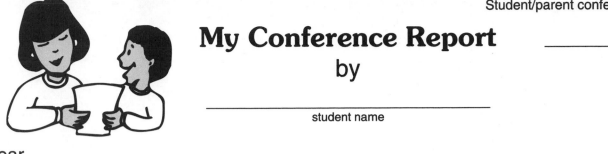

My Conference Report
by

_____
date

_____
student name

Dear _____,

I know that learning is important. I can help myself learn by taking a look at myself.

I can look at my work. I know when I do my best. I also know when I need to do a better job. Thinking about it helps me to see the things I do well. It helps me to know if I should try to do a better job.

Please read this report. Then tell me the ways you think I am doing a good job. Tell me what you like about my ideas, too. This will help me to enjoy learning.

Thank you for caring about me.

Your child,

_____

This is how I see myself! I have circled the faces that show my feelings.

1. I listen and follow directions.
2. My work is neat and easy to read.
3. I finish my work on time.
4. I take care of my belongings.
5. I am helpful to others.
6. I keep my hands and feet to myself.
7. I raise my hand before talking in class.
8. I try to do my best.
9. I am willing to fix my problems.
10. I like coming to school.

Here is what I will do to improve.

I will _____

I will _____

My Conference Report
by

_____
date

_____
student name

Dear _____,

   I know that by taking a look at myself I can evaluate my work habits and behavior. Evaluating helps me to see the things I do well. It also helps me to identify the things that I need to improve.

   This is my evaluation of how I see my work habits and my behavior at school. Please read this report. Then tell me the ways you think I am doing a good job. Also tell me what you like about my plans to improve.

   Thank you for caring about me!

Your child,

_____

Work Habits (Check the statement that best describes your school work.)

1. ❏ I always finish my work.   2. ❏ I study a lot.
    ❏ I usually finish my work.   ❏ I study sometimes.
    ❏ I rarely finish my work.   ❏ I study very little.

Behavior And Attitude

3. In class my behavior is   4. I think learning is
    ❏ helpful.   ❏ easy.
    ❏ sometimes helpful.   ❏ difficult at times.
    ❏ distracting to others.   ❏ very difficult.

Three things I can do to improve are:

1. _____

2. _____

3. _____

Missed Assignments

_____ date

Dear Parent,

_____ needs to

complete the following assignments:

_____

_____

_____

_____ .

This work is due by _____

Your help and support are greatly appreciated.

Sincerely,

_____
teacher signature

_____
parent signature

Please sign and return.

Missed Assignments

_____ date

Dear Parent,

_____ needs to

complete the following assignments:

_____

_____

_____

_____ .

This work is due by _____

Your help and support are greatly appreciated.

Sincerely,

_____
teacher signature

_____
parent signature

Please sign and return.

_____
date

Incomplete Work

Dear Parent,

_____ needs to
complete the following assignments:

_____

_____

_____

_____ .

This work is due by _____ .

Your help and support are greatly appreciated.

_____
teacher signature

_____
parent signature

Please sign and return.

©The Education Center, Inc. • TEC802

_____
date

Incomplete Work

Dear Parent,

_____ needs to
complete the following assignments:

_____

_____

_____

_____ .

This work is due by _____ .

Your help and support are greatly appreciated.

_____
teacher signature

_____
parent signature

Please sign and return.

©The Education Center, Inc. • TEC802

Notice Of Overdue Assignments

_____
date

Dear Parent,

Your child, _____, has the following overdue assignments:

_____

_____

_____

_____

If not completed, this missing work may affect your child's grades. These assignments are due on _____.

Thank you,

_____
teacher signature

_____
parent signature

Please sign and return.

©The Education Center, Inc. • TEC802

Notice Of Overdue Assignments

_____
date

Dear Parent,

Your child, _____, has the following overdue assignments:

_____

_____

_____

_____

If not completed, this missing work may affect your child's grades. These assignments are due on _____.

Thank you,

_____
teacher signature

_____
parent signature

Please sign and return.

©The Education Center, Inc. • TEC802

Extra Help Needed

_____
date

Dear Parent,

_____ needs extra help with _____

_____.

Here are some suggestions for how you can
help your child at home:

_____

_____

_____

_____

Thank you.

Sincerely,

_____
teacher signature

- -

Extra Help Needed

_____
date

Dear Parent,

_____ needs extra help with _____

_____.

Here are some suggestions for how you can
help your child at home:

_____

_____

_____

Thank you.

Sincerely,

_____
teacher signature

A Note of Concern

_____
date

Dear Parent,

I am concerned about your child, _____,

because _____

_____

_____

Here are some suggestions:

_____

_____

Please call me at school if you would like to discuss this further.

Sincerely,

_____
teacher signature

GLUE

COLORFUL CRAYONS

8 LARGE CRAYONS

8 LARGE CRAYONS

©The Education Center, Inc. • TEC802

A Note of Concern

_____
date

Dear Parent,

I am concerned about your child, _____,

because _____

_____

_____

Here are some suggestions:

_____

_____

Please call me at school if you would like to discuss this further.

Sincerely,

_____
teacher signature

GLUE

COLORFUL CRAYONS

8 LARGE CRAYONS

8 LARGE CRAYONS

©The Education Center, Inc. • TEC802

We're Going On A Field Trip!

Dear Parent,

We are planning a trip to

_____

on _____, _____. Your child will need to

bring: • field trip permission form (below)

                • _____

                • _____

                • _____

Keep this note and post it at home as a reminder. Thank you.

_____
teacher signature

Cut here and return the form below.

_____ has my permission to go on

the field trip to _____,

scheduled on _____.

_____
parent signature

_____
date

Note To Teacher: Duplicate one copy of this page and program the necessary information. Then duplicate copies for your students' parents.

Special Event Field Trip

Dear Parent,

Our class has the opportunity to visit _____
location

on _____. This experience will enrich your child's
date

knowledge of _____.

Your child will need to bring:

- field trip permission slip (below)
- _____
- _____

We will leave at _____and return by _____.

Keep this note and post it at home as a reminder. Thank you.

Sincerely,

_____
teacher signature

Cut here and return the form below.   ©The Education Center, Inc. • TEC802

_____ has my permission to go on the field trip to _____
location

on _____.
date

_____   _____
parent signature   date

Special Event Field Trip

Dear Parent,

Our class has the opportunity to visit _____
location

on _____. This experience will enrich your child's
date

knowledge of _____.

Your child will need to bring:

- field trip permission slip (below)
- _____
- _____

We will leave at _____and return by _____.

Keep this note and post it at home as a reminder. Thank you.

Sincerely,

_____
teacher signature

Cut here and return the form below.   ©The Education Center, Inc. • TEC802

_____ has my permission to go on the field trip to _____
location

on _____.
date

_____   _____
parent signature   date

Note To Teacher: Duplicate one copy of this page and program the necessary information. Then duplicate copies for your students' parents.

Permission to stay after school

Dear Parent,

    We will be participating in the following activity which involves some time after school: _____

_____

    Your child is welcome to participate on _____

from _____ to _____.
         time   time

    Please complete the form below granting your permission. Return it to school with your child. Thank you.

_____
date

Sincerely,

_____
teacher signature

Cut here and return the form below.   ©The Education Center, Inc. • TEC802

- -

_____ has my permission to stay after school on _____

from _____ to _____. I have made arrangements to
     time   time   date

❑ have my child picked up by _____.
                                person

❑ have my child walk home.

_____
parent signature

_____
date

- -

Dear Parent,

    We will be participating in the following activity which involves some time after school: _____

_____

    Your child is welcome to participate on _____

from _____ to _____.
         time   time

    Please complete the form below granting your permission. Return it to school with your child. Thank you.

_____
date

Sincerely,

_____
teacher signature

Cut here and return the form below.   ©The Education Center, Inc. • TEC802

- -

_____ has my permission to stay after school on _____

from _____ to _____. I have made arrangements to
     time   time   date

❑ have my child picked up by _____.
                                person

❑ have my child walk home.

_____
parent signature

_____
date

- -

132   **Note To Teacher:** Duplicate one copy of this page and program the necessary information. Then duplicate copies for your students' parents.

Money Due

Dear Parent,

_____ owes
student

_____ for _____.
amount   reason

Please return the money to school in this envelope by

_____.

Sincerely,

_____
teacher signature

©The Education Center, Inc. • TEC802

Money Due

Dear Parent,

_____ owes
student

_____ for _____.
amount   reason

Please return the money to school in this envelope by

_____.

Sincerely,

_____
teacher signature

©The Education Center, Inc. • TEC802

Money Due

Dear Parent,

_____ owes
student

_____ for _____.
amount   reason

Please return the money to school in this envelope by

_____.

Sincerely,

_____
teacher signature

©The Education Center, Inc. • TEC802

Note To Teacher: Duplicate a supply of money due forms. Cut the forms apart and attach each one to the front of an envelope. Program each form with the necessary information before sending it home.

We're Having A Special Program

Event: _____

Date: _____

Time: _____

Place: _____

You can help us by _____

_____

_____

_____

Sincerely,

_____
teacher signature

©The Education Center, Inc. • TEC802

We're Having A Special Program

Event: _____

Date: _____

Time: _____

Place: _____

You can help us by _____

_____

_____

_____

Sincerely,

_____
teacher signature

©The Education Center, Inc. • TEC802

Note To Teacher: Duplicate one copy of this page and program the necessary information. Then duplicate copies to distribute to parents or staff members.

Special TV Program

Dear Parent,
    Here's a program worth watching with your child.
It is recommended because _____
_____ .

Program: _____

Date: _____ Time: _____ Channel: _____

Comments: _____

_____

Sincerely,

_____
teacher signature

©The Education Center, Inc. • TEC802

Special TV Program

Dear Parent,
    Here's a program worth watching with your child.
It is recommended because _____
_____ .

Program: _____

Date: _____ Time: _____ Channel: _____

Comments: _____

_____

Sincerely,

_____
teacher signature

©The Education Center, Inc. • TEC802

Note To Teacher: Duplicate one copy of this page and program the necessary information. Then duplicate copies for your students' parents.

Injury Report

_____
date

Dear Parent,

This is to report that _____ was
student

injured at school.

Injury: _____

Treatment: _____

Treated by: _____

Follow-up suggestions: _____

_____

Please sign and return this notice. Thank you.

_____   _____
parent signature   teacher signature

©The Education Center, Inc. • TEC802

Injury Report

_____
date

Dear Parent,

This is to report that _____ was
student

injured at school.

Injury: _____

Treatment: _____

Treated by: _____

Follow-up suggestions: _____

_____

Please sign and return this notice. Thank you.

_____   _____
parent signature   teacher signature

©The Education Center, Inc. • TEC802

Broken Rule Notice

_____
date

Dear Parent,

Your child, _____, has broken a school rule by: _____

_____

The following disciplinary action was taken at school: _____

_____

Your child's plan for improved behavior includes _____

_____

It is important to us that all of our students have a positive and successful learning environment. Please support our efforts by visiting with your child to encourage appropriate behavior.

Please sign this notice and return it to school. If you have any questions concerning this notice, please contact me. Thank you.

Sincerely,

Comments: _____   _____
teacher signature

_____

_____

_____   _____
parent signature

©The Education Center, Inc. • TEC802

Broken Rule Notice

_____
date

Dear Parent,

Your child, _____, has broken a school rule by: _____

_____

The following disciplinary action was taken at school: _____

_____

Your child's plan for improved behavior includes _____

_____

It is important to us that all of our students have a positive and successful learning environment. Please support our efforts by visiting with your child to encourage appropriate behavior.

Please sign this notice and return it to school. If you have any questions concerning this notice, please contact me. Thank you.

Sincerely,

Comments: _____   _____
teacher signature

_____

_____

_____   _____
parent signature

©The Education Center, Inc. • TEC802

No School Notice

Dear Parent,

    Please note that school will not be in session on _____
                                                                    date

due to _____.
                                            reason

School will resume on _____, _____.
                           day   date

Sincerely,

_____
teacher signature

©The Education Center, Inc. • TEC802

No School Notice

Dear Parent,

    Please note that school will not be in session on _____
                                                                    date

due to _____.
                                            reason

School will resume on _____, _____.
                           day   date

Sincerely,

_____
teacher signature

©The Education Center, Inc. • TEC802

Note To Teacher: Duplicate one copy of this page and program the necessary information. Then duplicate copies for your students' parents.

Dear Parent,

_____ needs the following

school supplies:

_____ pencils
_____ paper
_____ crayons
_____ glue
_____ other: _____

_____

_____

_____

_____ teacher signature

GLUE

COLORFUL CRAYONS

©The Education Center, Inc. • TEC802

Dear Parent,

_____ needs the following

school supplies:

_____ pencils
_____ paper
_____ crayons
_____ glue
_____ other: _____

_____

_____

_____

_____ teacher signature

GLUE

COLORFUL CRAYONS

©The Education Center, Inc. • TEC802

Note To Teacher: Duplicate one copy of this page and program the necessary information. Then duplicate copies for your students' parents.

School Supplies

Dear Parent,

_____ needs

the following school supplies:

_____ pencils ☐ No. 2 ☐ red
_____ pens ☐ black ☐ blue ☐ red
_____ markers ☐ all colors ☐ _____
_____ colored pencils
_____ crayons
_____ notebook paper ☐ wide ruled ☐ college ruled
                        ☐ narrow ruled
_____ 3-ring notebook
_____ spiral notebook with _____ pages
_____ folder ☐ with pockets ☐ with brads
_____ other: _____

Thank you,

_____
teacher signature

©The Education Center, Inc. • TEC802

School Supplies

Dear Parent,

_____ needs

the following school supplies:

_____ pencils ☐ No. 2 ☐ red
_____ pens ☐ black ☐ blue ☐ red
_____ markers ☐ all colors ☐ _____
_____ colored pencils
_____ crayons
_____ notebook paper ☐ wide ruled ☐ college ruled
                        ☐ narrow ruled
_____ 3-ring notebook
_____ spiral notebook with _____ pages
_____ folder ☐ with pockets ☐ with brads
_____ other: _____

Thank you,

_____
teacher signature

©The Education Center, Inc. • TEC802

Note To Teacher: Duplicate this page and program the necessary information. Then duplicate copies for your students' parents.

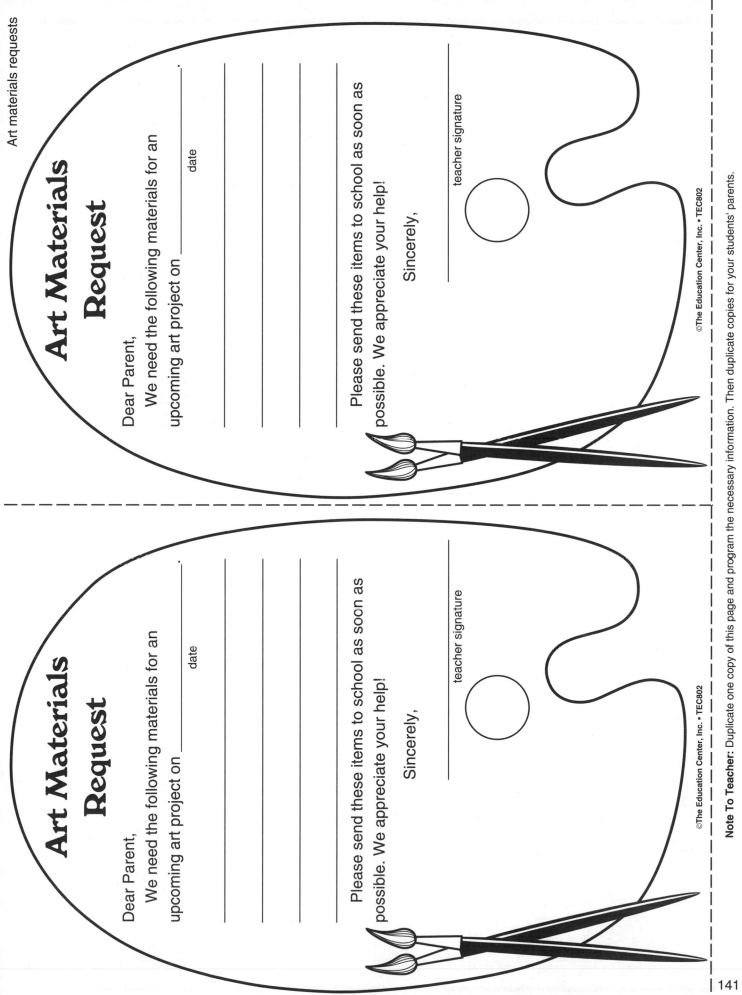

Art Materials Request

Dear Parent,
We need the following materials for an
upcoming art project on _____ .
                                    date

_____

_____

_____

_____

Please send these items to school as soon as
possible. We appreciate your help!

Sincerely,

_____
teacher signature

©The Education Center, Inc. • TEC802

Art Materials Request

Dear Parent,
We need the following materials for an
upcoming art project on _____ .
                                    date

_____

_____

_____

_____

Please send these items to school as soon as
possible. We appreciate your help!

Sincerely,

_____
teacher signature

©The Education Center, Inc. • TEC802

Note To Teacher: Duplicate one copy of this page and program the necessary information. Then duplicate copies for your students' parents.

141

Special Project Supplies

Dear Parent,
We need your help. We are doing a special project related to _____ .
                        subject-lesson-class

Your child needs to bring the following items

by _____ .
        date

_____

_____

_____

_____

Thanks for helping!

_____
teacher signature

GLUE

Special Project Supplies

Dear Parent,
We need your help. We are doing a special project related to _____ .
                        subject-lesson-class

Your child needs to bring the following items

by _____ .
        date

_____

_____

_____

_____

Thanks for helping!

_____
teacher signature

GLUE

Note To Teacher: Duplicate one copy of this page and program the necessary information. Then duplicate copies for your students' parents.

Just A Reminder

to _____
name

Please remember _____
_____
_____
_____

Due by _____

_____
teacher signature

Just A Reminder

to _____
name

Please remember _____
_____
_____
_____

Due by _____

_____
teacher signature

Just A Reminder

to _____
name

Please remember _____
_____
_____
_____

Due by _____

_____
teacher signature

Just A Reminder

to _____
name

Please remember _____
_____
_____
_____

Due by _____

_____
teacher signature

Our Class Newsletter

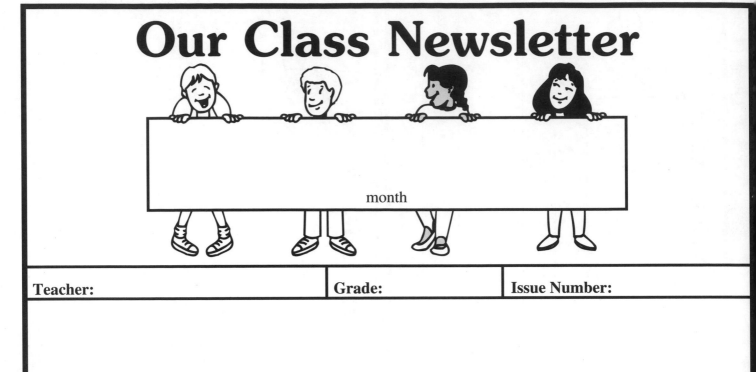

month

Teacher:	Grade:	Issue Number:

Note To Teacher: Duplicate one copy of this page and record your monthly class events. Then duplicate copies for your students.

Parent Volunteer Information

Dear Parent,

It is helpful for me to gather information about my students' parents for upcoming projects and events. I value your interests and expertise, and I encourage you to share your talents with us. Please complete the form below and return it to school as soon as possible.

Sincerely,

_____

teacher signature

- -

Parent _____ Child _____

Address _____ Phone _____

I enjoy the following hobbies: _____

My profession is _____

I can contribute by

❑ being a parent helper ❑ making phone calls ❑ going on field trips

❑ supplying materials ❑ making projects at home ❑ other _____

Comments: _____

_____

©The Education Center, Inc. • TEC802

Parent Volunteer Information

Dear Parent,

It is helpful for me to gather information about my students' parents for upcoming projects and events. I value your interests and expertise, and I encourage you to share your talents with us. Please complete the form below and return it to school as soon as possible.

Sincerely,

_____

teacher signature

- -

Parent _____ Child _____

Address _____ Phone _____

I enjoy the following hobbies: _____

My profession is _____

I can contribute by

❑ being a parent helper ❑ making phone calls ❑ going on field trips

❑ supplying materials ❑ making projects at home ❑ other _____

Comments: _____

_____

©The Education Center, Inc. • TEC802

You're Invited!

Dear Parent,

You are invited to

_____
event

at our school at _____ on _____,
time   day

_____. We hope to see you there!
date

Sincerely,

_____
teacher signature

©The Education Center, Inc. • TEC802

You're Invited!

Dear Parent,

You are invited to

_____
event

at our school at _____ on _____,
time   day

_____. We hope to see you there!
date

Sincerely,

_____
teacher signature

©The Education Center, Inc. • TEC802

Note To Teacher: Duplicate this page and program the necessary information. Then duplicate copies for your students' parents.

Halloween Party!

Dear Parent,

Our Halloween party will be

at _____
time

on _____, _____.
day   date

We will celebrate by _____

_____.

If you would like to help, please check one
of the boxes below and return this note to school.

❑ I will provide snacks.   ❑ I will help in the classroom.

❑ other _____

Sincerely,

_____   _____
parent signature   teacher signature

©The Education Center, Inc. • TEC802

- -

Halloween Party!

Dear Parent,

Our Halloween party will be

at _____
time

on _____, _____.
day   date

We will celebrate by _____

_____.

If you would like to help, please check one
of the boxes below and return this note to school.

❑ I will provide snacks.   ❑ I will help in the classroom.

❑ other _____

Sincerely,

_____   _____
parent signature   teacher signature

©The Education Center, Inc. • TEC802

Note To Teacher: Duplicate one copy of this page and program the necessary information. Then duplicate copies for your students' parents.

A Christmas Party

Dear Parent,

Our Christmas party will be at _____
time

on _____, _____.
day   date

If you would like to contribute, please check one of
the following items:

❑ food _____   ❑ napkins
❑ drink _____   ❑ cups
❑ party favors
❑ other _____

We have _____ students in our class.
Thank you!

_____
teacher signature

_____   _____
child's name   parent signature

©The Education Center, Inc. • TEC802

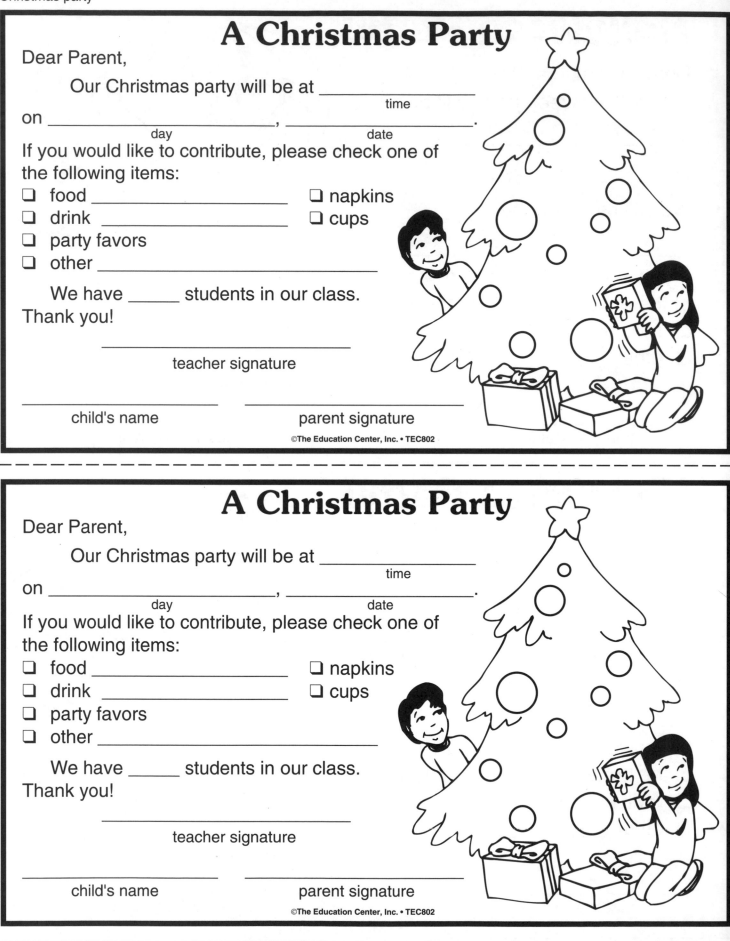

A Christmas Party

Dear Parent,

Our Christmas party will be at _____
time

on _____, _____.
day   date

If you would like to contribute, please check one of
the following items:

❑ food _____   ❑ napkins
❑ drink _____   ❑ cups
❑ party favors
❑ other _____

We have _____ students in our class.
Thank you!

_____
teacher signature

_____   _____
child's name   parent signature

©The Education Center, Inc. • TEC802

Note To Teacher: Duplicate one copy of this page and program the necessary information. Then duplicate copies for your students' parents.

Dear Parent,

Our Valentine party will be at

_____ on _____,
        time   day

_____.
            date

We will celebrate by _____

_____

_____.

If you would like to help, please check one
of the boxes below and return this portion
of the form to school.

❑ I will provide snacks.

❑ other _____

❑ I will help in the classroom.

Sincerely,

_____   _____
     parent signature   teacher signature

Class List

_____   _____
_____   _____
_____   _____
_____   _____
_____   _____
_____   _____
_____   _____
_____   _____
_____   _____
_____   _____
_____   _____
_____   _____

©The Education Center, Inc. • TEC802

We're Celebrating!

Dear Parent,

We are celebrating _____

_____

at _____ on _____,

time · day

_____. Please help us

date

celebrate by _____

_____

_____

_____

Thank you!   Sincerely,

_____

teacher signature

©The Education Center, Inc. • TEC802

We're Celebrating!

Dear Parent,

We are celebrating _____

_____

at _____ on _____,

time · day

_____. Please help us

date

celebrate by _____

_____

_____

_____

Thank you!   Sincerely,

_____

teacher signature

©The Education Center, Inc. • TEC802

Note To Teacher: Duplicate one copy of this page and program the necessary information. Then duplicate copies for your students' parents.

To: _____

Please get well soon. We really miss you!

Your teacher,

_____

©The Education Center, Inc. • TEC802

Note To Teacher: Duplicate this page to send home as coloring projects for ill students.

Dear _____,

Thank you for _____

_____

_____

_____

_____

Your friend,

_____

Thank You

From our
point of view,
it was very nice
of you!

Sincerely,

_____

MAKING TRACKS!

Watch _____ go!

You have really improved in

_____

_____ teacher signature

_____ date

©The Education Center, Inc. • TEC802

MAKING TRACKS!

Watch _____ go!

You have really improved in

_____

_____ teacher signature

_____ date

©The Education Center, Inc. • TEC802

Achievement Award

to

_____

for

_____

_____
teacher signature

_____
date

Achievement Award

to

_____

for

_____

_____
teacher signature

_____
date

Building

SUCCESS

This is to certify that _____

_____

_____   _____
teacher signature   date

©The Education Center, Inc. • TEC802

Building

SUCCESS

This is to certify that _____

_____

_____   _____
teacher signature   date

©The Education Center, Inc. • TEC802

Three Cheers For

_____
student

for

_____

_____

_____

Hip, Hip, Hurray!

_____
teacher signature

_____
date

©The Education Center, Inc. • TEC802

Three Cheers For

_____
student

for

_____

_____

_____

Hip, Hip, Hurray!

_____
teacher signature

_____
date

©The Education Center, Inc. • TEC802

Hey, _____!

You're on a roll
for

_____

_____

_____

_____

_____   _____
teacher signature   date

Hey, _____!

You're on a roll
for

_____

_____

_____

_____

_____   _____
teacher signature   date

"DINO-MITE" ATTENDANCE

This is to report that

_____
student

has had perfect attendance for

_____.
period of time

Keep up the good work!

_____
teacher signature

©The Education Center, Inc. • TEC802

"DINO-MITE" ATTENDANCE

This is to report that

_____
student

has had perfect attendance for

_____.
period of time

Keep up the good work!

_____
teacher signature

©The Education Center, Inc. • TEC802

Certificate Of Promotion

This is to certify that

_____

has successfully completed _____

and has been promoted to _____

Congratulations to you!

_____
date

_____
teacher signature

_____
principal signature

This is to certify that

----

has successfully completed

----

and has been promoted to

Congratulations!

----

teacher signature

----

date